A Taste of
THE LIVERPOOL WAY
A RECIPE FOR SUCCESS

A Taste of
THE LIVERPOOL WAY

A RECIPE FOR SUCCESS

Reach Sport

A Taste of
THE LIVERPOOL WAY
A RECIPE FOR SUCCESS

Hardback edition first published in Great Britain in 2021
www.reachsport.com
@reach_sport
Reach Sport is a part of Reach PLC Ltd, 5 St Paul's Square, Liverpool, L3 9SJ
One Canada Square, Canary Wharf, London, E15 5AP

Hardback ISBN: 9781911613961
Photographic acknowledgements:
Liverpool FC Getty Images, Mirrorpix, PA, Alamy, UnSplash
Editor: David Cottrell
Design: Rick Cooke, Ben Renshaw, Lee Ashun, Chris Collins
Production Editor: Michael McGuinness
Writers: David Cottrell, William Hughes, Chris Brereton
Language translations: Premier Language Solutions
Seasonal produce advice: Greens of Oxton
Cover: Rick Cooke

Printed and bound by Bell & Bain

AXA TRAINING CENTRE

JÜRGEN KLOPP

"MONA IS A TRANSFORMATIVE FIGURE FOR PROFESSIONAL FOOTBALL AND I AM DELIGHTED THAT SHE IS PRODUCING THIS BOOK"

I was once asked to name the best signing I've ever made during my time as a football manager and the answer I gave was Mona Nemmer!

Of course there was an element of humour about this, but the truth is I actually can't name anyone better.

I didn't know Mona when I worked in Germany, but I had heard of her reputation. The importance of nutrition to professional athletes was becoming more obvious and I wanted the very best for Liverpool Football Club.

I asked players, coaches and managers from around the world and the same name coming back: Mona!

If her reputation and credentials were impressive, it was nothing compared to when I actually got to work with her first-hand and see her in action.

Mona is a transformative figure for professional football. Her commitment to learning is mind-blowing. Her hunger for knowledge and new ideas is never satisfied. I can honestly say I don't think I have met a more relentless individual when it comes to innovation.

But, as any coach or leader of people will tell you, having knowledge is one thing...imparting it to others is what really matters and this is where she excels.

Her ability to influence and educate the players and staff makes her one of the most valuable team-members at LFC.

I am delighted that she is producing this book so our supporters around the world will have the opportunity to benefit from her remarkable work.

This gives our fans the chance to learn from Mona, just as our players do.

You'll Never Walk Alone

Jürgen

"HAVING KNOWLEDGE IS ONE THING BUT IMPARTING IT TO OTHERS IS WHAT REALLY MATTERS AND THIS IS WHERE MONA EXCELS — HER ABILITY TO INFLUENCE AND EDUCATE THE PLAYERS AND STAFF MAKES HER ONE OF THE MOST VALUABLE TEAM-MEMBERS AT LIVERPOOL FC"

JÜRGEN KLOPP

CONTENTS

An online hub enabling supporters to find out more about the club's contribution to a more sustainable future can be found at liverpoolfc.com/TheRedWay.

MEET MONA NEMMER

—

"FOOTBALLERS MUST PREPARE THE BEST WAY BEFORE AND AFTER EACH MATCH AND WHAT WE PUT INTO OUR BODIES IS KEY TO THIS. BUT NUTRITION IS ABOUT MORE THAN FOOD-INTAKE – IT'S ABOUT HOW FOOD IS PREPARED AND PRESENTED AND HOW THAT PLAYS INTO OUR HEALTH AND WELLBEING"

Hello readers! My job at Liverpool Football Club is to make sure the players eat the right food at the right times. My dream is to help the next generation of fans and footballers learn more about where good food comes from, why a healthy, well-balanced diet improves our wellbeing and sporting performance, and how it can be simple, easy and affordable to grow our own produce and even cook our own meals.

I'm originally from Germany where I worked for the German national team and Bayern Munich before I was appointed LFC's head of nutrition in the summer of 2016. I soon fell in love with the football club, the fans, the city.

I feel blessed because it's the hardest thing on earth to find a job which gives you so much satisfaction and you can actually integrate your work into what you love to do.

There is a special atmosphere here at the club and in the city which makes you feel welcome and at home. Working closely with so many friendly, talented, passionate people is an absolute privilege. This book – I really hope – is a little way of giving something back.

I love good food too! But as well as all those lovely flavours and tastes, it's the science which fascinates me – and in particular how the theory behind nutrition can be applied practically to our busy lifestyles and what we eat every day.

It's still quite a 'young' subject so we are learning all the time about new developments and ideas.

Playing football, among other things, is about endurance and strength. To have both and to 'feed your need' when you exercise, you must prepare the best way before and after a match. What you put into your body is key to this. It's about having the right balance of carbohydrates (for energy), protein (for strength) and vitamins and minerals (for good health). Not forgetting regular hydration of course!

At Liverpool FC there is so much history and tradition but also a modern, open-minded perspective among the players, management and staff which has helped to give nutrition a great profile and lots of respect and makes my job so fulfilling.

Jürgen Klopp is the reason for this because he gives us a real family vibe at LFC, along with the opportunity and freedom to work hard and responsibly and achieve the highest standards we possibly can. He's a very smart leader who empowers, supports and pushes you in equal measure. None of it is possible without him. It's incredible to work with him and for him.

I remember chatting with Jürgen when I first arrived, during a pre-season summer tour in America, and rather than introduce myself to the team I asked if we could let the buffet speak for itself. The players didn't just eat quickly and leave – they spent longer over their food choices, they were interested in what was there. That first impression was so important and was so lovely to see.

It's the same when we go to a restaurant, isn't it? We know immediately if we want to stay there, based on what we see (sometimes on other people's plates!) and how it makes us feel. That's why nutrition is about more than food-intake. It's about how the food is prepared and presented, too, and how that plays into our health and wellbeing. And the more colours there are, the higher the amount of massively beneficial micro-nutrients there usually is.

Colours are everywhere in the canteen at the AXA Training Centre in Kirkby.

We want it to have the feel of a 'marketplace' where the players can pick and choose which salads or juices, for example, they want. Again, it's not just a place where food-intake is happening – it's the heart of the AXA Training Centre, a homely and happy environment where people love to stay and chill or chat about football, family, friends, anything.

How we present the food is part of the pleasure. It helps the players to make the best decisions about what they eat, so they understand what their bodies require and how healthy food enables them to perform in training and on matchdays and recover in the best possible way.

We call this 'product knowledge'. So even if you are not too familiar with the subject of nutrition, you can still learn to make a decision about what to have on your plate, based on what you know and how the food is prepared. It's better than someone telling you, "It's okay to have this because it's healthy but you can't have that because it's bad for you."

It's not as simple as that, and it shouldn't be so strict or scary or make you feel guilty. It should be a positive and empowering process, whether it's deciding on the food on the supermarket shelves for your basket or the food in the kitchen for the plate in front of you.

For instance, if you fry a potato it might taste nice but it might also lose a lot of the nutritional value. Or if you choose a lighter-coloured chocolate, it simply means more sugar and more milk has been added.

But you could bake or steam the potato instead, go for the darker chocolate as an occasional treat. Use that product knowledge!

The idea for this book came before the pandemic. But even in those pre-COVID-19 days there was – and still is – an epidemic of childhood obesity.

Now more than ever it's important that we all try to eat well and exercise regularly not only to keep fit and stay in shape but to boost our immune systems. A healthy diet means a healthy body and good mental health too.

By buying fresh, local, seasonal produce where and whenever possible, we are also supporting our own community. Local food suppliers and businesses will benefit while we reduce our 'food miles', plastic packaging and our 'carbon footprint' – helping to create a sustainable future for us all. Little changes really can make a big difference.

Football's world governing body, FIFA, says that it is crucial for aspiring young footballers to "develop the domestic skills and nutrition knowledge that will allow them to reach their full potential as players."

In this book I hope that you will learn about food types and the good things they can provide for our bodies, and even what some famous names in the Liverpool FC dressing-room have learnt about nutrition; discover how we recognise and tell the difference between tastes and flavours; explore ways to prepare ingredients and preserve them to last longer; and also find out why growing our own fruit and vegetables is the gift which keeps giving all year round. Plus a few easy and cost-effective recipes with an Anfield twist!

Get informed. Feel inspired. And above all, have fun!

Mona

"IN THIS BOOK I HOPE THAT YOU WILL LEARN ABOUT FOOD TYPES AND THE GOOD THINGS THEY CAN PROVIDE FOR OUR BODIES, AND EVEN WHAT SOME FAMOUS NAMES IN THE LIVERPOOL FC DRESSING-ROOM HAVE LEARNT ABOUT NUTRITION; EXPLORE WAYS TO PREPARE INGREDIENTS AND PRESERVE THEM TO LAST LONGER; AND ALSO FIND OUT WHY GROWING OUR OWN FRUIT AND VEGETABLES IS THE GIFT WHICH KEEPS GIVING ALL YEAR ROUND"

NUTRITION COMPASS

 Fats

Saturated and unsaturated
Store energy and protect organs

 Protein

Animal and plant-based
Develop and repair muscles

 Carbohydriates

Simple and complex
Provide fuel and energy

MACRO NUTRIENTS

MICRO NUTRIENTS

 Vitamins

Fat-soluble and water-soluble, for example A, B, C, D, E, K

 Minerals

For example Mg, K, Ca, Fe, Se, Na, I, P, Cu, Mn

 Fibre

Soluble and insoluble

 Antioxdants

For example polyphenols and carotenoids

WAYS TO GO

MACRO-NUTRIENTS AND MICRO-NUTRIENTS – THE BIG PICTURE AND THE LITTLE DETAILS – AND WHY IT'S SO IMPORTANT FOR US ALL TO STAY HYDRATED

Take a look at our 'Nutrition Compass' on the left, designed to help you understand simply what kinds of incredible nutrients there are, how they contribute towards our daily health and general wellbeing, and just some of the amazing foods in which you can find them.

As you can see, our guide to nutrition has several different 'compass points', each with its own role to play in keeping us in maximum physical and mental shape. But one or even two directions is not enough – like footballers and other athletes we need to balance our bearings to enjoy the healthiest, most beneficial modern-day lifestyle.

What's the other big thing that stands out? The different colours, right? As a rule, the more natural colours you have on your plate, the better for your body.

From fruits and vegetables, to meat and fish, to dairy produce, to nuts and seeds, and to pasta, rice and bread...they all contain at least one and sometimes a combination of what we call macro-nutrients and micro-nutrients. This chapter explains what they are, their value to our bodies and where we can find them. You'd be surprised at how easy it is to develop a good basic knowledge and you'll be delighted (we hope!) by the difference it can make in so many ways – not least in your sporting performance.

As Liverpool manager Jürgen Klopp himself says: "We are all looking for the extra edge. How can we be better than the opponent we will battle with? By following the guidance of our experts you can put the very best fuel in your engines. The right nutrition can be the difference, but like everything else in elite sport, you need to do the right things and follow the best advice."

SO THESE ARE THE MAIN HEADLINES ABOUT
THE NUTRIENTS WE CAN FIND IN OUR FOOD:

MACRO-NUTRIENTS

These are the nutrients required in large
amounts and the body's three main
energy sources, each with an important
role to play in keeping us fit and healthy.

CARBOHYDRATES

Can be simple
or complex.
Provide fuel
and energy.

PROTEIN

Can be animal or
plant-based.
Develop and repair
muscles.

FATS

Can be saturated or
unsaturated.
Store energy and
protect organs.

MICRO-NUTRIENTS

These are the many nutrients required in smaller amounts – 'trace elements' – and their job is to help the body recover better and boost the immune system.

VITAMINS

Can be fat-soluble or water-soluble. For example, A, B, C, D, E, K.

MINERALS

Zinc, magnesium, potassium, calcium, iron etc.

ANTIOXIDANTS

For example, polyphenols and carotenoids.

FIBRE

Can be soluble or insoluble.

HERE COME THE CARBS

GIVING US THE FUEL TO GO OUT THERE AND PERFORM!

On average a Premier League footballer can run around 12 km during the 90 minutes of a match. When Liverpool won the title in season 2019/20, midfielder James Milner covered a whopping 13.11 km (8.15 miles) during a 2-0 home win over Sheffield United.

Team-mate Roberto Firmino was in the Premier League's top five for distance covered throughout the whole season, his 301.88 km (188 miles) the equivalent of running over seven marathons!

Neither Milly or Bobby or any top footballer would be able to run so much if it wasn't for carbohydrates – their main source of energy with an important role in a healthy, balanced diet.

WHAT THEY ARE…

Carbohydrates are energy-deliverers in the body, and their 'fuel' is stored in our muscles and organs. They come in two types: simple and complex.

Simple or 'whiter' carbs are ingested by the body rapidly and so release their energy quickly. They are also known as high GI carbohydrates, with the 'GI' standing for glycaemic index – a rating system for the speed at which each type of food affects your blood-sugar level when it is eaten. Complex or low GI carbs, on the other hand, are stored for longer and release energy more slowly and steadily.

Think of it like this: simple carbs as a piece of paper thrown into a fire, burning brightly and quickly; and complex ones as logs on the same fire, taking longer to burn and giving off more heat and energy over time.

WHAT THEY DO…

In basic footballing terms, carbs provide the fuel for playing. They are stored within the muscles and liver as glycogen which is then used during training and matches to allow muscles to function effectively.

8.15 MILES

MILLY'S MILES

James Milner once covered a whopping 13.11 km (8.15 miles) during a 2-0 home win over Sheffield United in the Premier League

In a whole PL season Bobby Firmino ran 188 miles – the same as running seven marathons

The amount you need each day depends on your height, weight, and of course how active you are. Ethnicity can also play a role. As a rule, you should eat more simple carbs for when you're exercising or in action and less when you're resting.

Complex carbs, meanwhile, are full of 'fibre structures' which are good for our digestion and wellbeing but can bother our bellies on matchdays. And too few carbs generally can lead to a lack of energy during exercise and a loss of concentration. It's all in the planning!

We'll look at this in more detail later on, but for a period of intense physical activity you might have more carbs on your plate in the form of rice, for example, with smaller, equal amounts of, say, chicken and vegetables. The less intense the activity, the less rice on the plate and more chicken and vegetables.

Mo Salah has the energy to play consistently at the highest level

WHERE TO FIND THEM…

Carbohydrates are mainly found in what are called 'starchy' foods such as potatoes, bread, rice, pasta and cereals (although carbs also include sugar and fibre). According to the NHS *Eatwell Guide*, they should make up just over a third of the food you eat.

You can also find them in couscous, quinoa, oats, corn and other grains like rye and barley, as well as vegetables like butternut squash, beans and peas, dried and tinned fruit, and bananas.

Potatoes are high GI carbs and also a good source of fibre (which we'll talk about later) when eaten with their skins on. The best carb-rich types of bread are wholemeal, granary, brown and seeded varieties.

Rice not only gives us energy through carbohydrates but it's also low in fat and good value for money. Among the many types of rice to choose from: arborio, basmati, long grain, brown, short grain and wild.

Pasta, a great source of carbohydrates, consists of dough made from durum wheat and water. And there are a lot of types out there, in various colours.

PROTEIN GIVES US POWER

BUILDING OUR STRENGTH BUT IT'S NOT JUST ABOUT THE MUSCLES!

Among the favourite recipes on the Liverpool FC menu are the '9:30', a dairy-free yoghurt, granola and fruit mix, and the 'Buttermilk Chicken'. They have one great thing in common: providing protein.

If carbs are great for energy reserves, proteins are crucial for strength. But that's not the only benefit. The right amount of protein enables the players who wear the famous red of LFC to repair muscles as well as build them, and in turn this can have a positive effect on our sleep quality and immune system.

It's important to know, too, that protein alone doesn't develop muscles – that comes through the right exercise and a diet containing not just protein but energy from a good balance of carbohydrates and fats.

AMINO ACIDS ARE ESSENTIAL

These are the building blocks of protein, and make up our cells, muscle and tissues

WHAT THEY ARE…

The word 'protein' originally comes from the Greek word *proteios*, meaning 'first place' or 'primary', which shows how important it is in our diet.

Proteins are made up of several types of amino acids. Think of them as the building blocks of protein, which combine in lots of different ways or 'chains' and are vital for the development of muscle tissue and repair.

Around half of all amino acids – we call them the 'essential' ones – can be consumed via the diet, and different sources of protein contain various amounts. 'Protein packages' can be as varied as a typical sirloin steak, a piece of grilled salmon, or a cup of cooked lentils.

As a rule, protein from animal sources tends to contain a wider variety of amino acids compared to those from plant-based groups. But either way, just like carbohydrates, proteins are one of the bases for all meals.

WHO CALLED IT PROTEIN?

A Dutch scientist called Gerhard Johann Mulder coined the word 'protein' way back in the 1830s, taking it from the original Greek word meaning 'holding first place'

WHAT THEY DO…

Protein is our cell-building substance, and the amino acids that we digest from proteins form building blocks for the body to make new muscle tissue and repair old or damaged tissue.

They also perform a similar function for hormones and enzymes that control different processes in

Brain

Skin

Lungs

Heart

Liver

Eggs and dairy products are an animal-based source of protein

the body such as regulating our metabolism, which is how our bodies convert what we eat and drink into energy.

Proteins, then, are super-important for the maintenance of muscle mass and for when footballers are recovering from training or playing in a match.

The longer the 'chain' of amino acids from proteins, the longer the digestion process, and research has shown that the most important factor is the timing of intake (rather than the total amount consumed) and the type of protein.

Lean meat and fish like salmon are often on the LFC menu

WHERE TO FIND THEM…

In ancient history, meat was the main source of protein for the first Olympic athletes, but today there is a huge range of protein-rich foods – both animal and plant-based.

Animal-based protein sources include all the essential amino acids that can only be obtained in the diet. Examples include lean meat such as chicken and turkey, eggs and dairy products like Greek yogurt, milk and cheese, and fish such as salmon, kippers, mackerel or even tuna.

Plant-based sources do not always contain all of the essential amino acids required by the body but they do contain high levels of other nutrients such as fibre. They include pulses (beans, lentils and peas), soy milk and tofu (also known as bean curd).

Animal-based sources tend to deliver a higher amount of protein than plant-based ones – for example, a 100g chicken breast has more protein than 100g of chickpeas – but the plant-based source is often easier to absorb, lower in cholesterol, and much more friendly to the planet.

Vegetarian or vegan footballers can consume an adequate amount of non-meat-based sources of protein as long as their diets are planned and followed carefully.

As always, it's about getting the right balance, and the wider the variety of sources the better. But try not to consume large quantities of 'processed' food products or 'junk' like nuggets, burgers, sausages, bacon and processed ham.

EVERYONE NEEDS FATS

JUST MAKE SURE THEY ARE THE RIGHT KIND IN THE RIGHT AMOUNTS!

'Fat' and 'football'. You wouldn't necessarily put those words together, it's fair to say. But the more you learn about fats, the more you realise that they're just as important to our fitness, health and wellbeing as all the other nutrients in this chapter – in the right amounts and from the correct sources.

In general, fats get a bad press and in some cases it's justified. But we shouldn't automatically think as them all as 'not allowed'. We need some types of fats because without them we can't survive.

It's true that as a nation we are consuming more 'fatty foods' and that some fats can raise our levels of cholesterol (see below) and increase the risk of heart disease and stroke. All fats are high in energy – more so than carbohydrates and protein – and this can lead to too many calories. Carbs and proteins both provide 4 calories per gram, while fat provides 9 calories per gram. It's also true that 'fatty acids' are an essential part of a healthy, balanced diet. These can't be made by the body itself and are responsible for a lot of functions including energy storage.

WHAT THEY ARE…

Most fats and oils contain both saturated (not so great, to be fair) and unsaturated (much better, as it goes) fats in different proportions.

Saturated fats mostly come from animal sources, including meat and dairy products, as well as some plant foods. They are often solid at room temperature, like the fat you see on a piece of steak or processed meat such as salami, and their intake in the UK diet is generally too high.

This can lead to an increase in cholesterol, a fatty substance mostly made by the body in the liver and transported in our blood. 'Cholesterol' is another one of those words which we think of as bad, and it's true that high amounts of 'low-density' cholesterol can cause a negative effect on health.

But there is also a 'high-density' version which has the positive effect of taking cholesterol from cells of the body where there's too much of it, to the liver, where it's disposed of. Confusing? A little bit!

Let's get on to the good stuff. Unsaturated fats are mostly found in oils from plants and fish, and their intake in the UK diet is generally too low. They come in two types: monounsaturated fats which help protect the heart and maintain

levels of good high-density cholesterol, and polyunsaturated fats which help lower levels of low-density cholesterol in the blood.

In turn, polyunsaturated fats can be divided into omega-3 and omega-6, which are both essential but can't be made by our bodies.

WHAT THEY DO…

Did you know there are some kinds of vitamins, like A, D, E and K, which are 'fat-soluble' – which means they can only be absorbed with the help of fats? Incidentally the name of one German supermarket brand containing those initials helps Mona to remember which ones!

Fats protect our organs, support cell growth and play an important role in biological processes such as hormone function, immunity, and reducing inflammation. They also give us energy – but any fat not used in these ways is converted into body fat. Indeed the same is true of carbs and proteins.

Like proteins, we have different 'chains' of fat. The longer they are, the better they are for our cardiovascular system (which permits blood to circulate and transport things like nutrients, oxygen and hormones to and from the cells in our body). A good way to imagine it is like a steam train moving smoothly along a railway line – it's the fats that help to make this happen and keep our bodies on the right track!

WHERE TO FIND THEM…

Foods high in saturated fats include fatty cuts of meat, sausages and pies and 'treats' like cakes and pastries, ice cream, chocolate sweets and biscuits.

Of the healthier options, monounsaturated fats are commonly found in avocados, olive oil, seeds and nuts.

Let's take one example. Linseed, also known as flax, has a great combination of omega-3 and omega-6. You can put a little spoonful of linseed oil in your breakfast or salad, for example, and soaked overnight the seeds ferment in a way that makes the protein (and amino acids) in them more digestible.

Polyunsaturated fats are found in foods from a more Mediterranean-based diet like oily fish, fruits and vegetables and some olive oil and vegetable oils.

Oily fish (good for omega-3) includes kippers, herring, trout, sardines, salmon and mackerel – known as salmonids and identified by a little fin on their back. For most households it's always nice to have two oils: one for frying at a higher temperature and another for cold foods, salad dressings and even juices.

THE 12TH MAN

TINY COLOURFUL HEROES MAKING SURE THE BODY RUNS LIKE CLOCKWORK!

We've learned about the big picture and macro-nutrients. Now it's time to look at the tiny details that make all the difference to how our bodies function and perform.

As the name suggests, micro-nutrients are the ones required in small or 'trace' amounts in food. But just because they are so tiny, it doesn't mean they're not absolutely vital to our health and wellbeing – they help various functions of the body to recover better and they boost the immune system.

Every hour of every day, our bodies are using micro-nutrients to provide us with energy, produce important enzymes and hormones, and prevent deficiencies.

Because of their size these many vitamins and minerals are not quite as familiar as the three main macro-nutrients, but they are present in most foods in different combinations and they have a special relationship with colour. Generally speaking, the more colour on your plate – not least from fruit and vegetables – the more beneficial for you.

All of us, whether we're budding athletes or not, can't afford to skip on them. FIFA's own *Nutrition for Football* guide states that "things like sports bars and liquid meal supplements can provide a compact and convenient way to consume carbohydrate and protein." But it adds that there is no substitute for the range of nutrients in "everyday foods" which are "likely to be just as effective and perhaps even better." The LFC philosophy is 'Food First'.

COMING OFF THE BENCH

Imagine the human body as a manager like Jürgen Klopp and micro-nutrients as a huddle of substitutes ready to join the action in a big match. He'd be telling them not just to get-stuck-in but to...
• Go out there (or rather, in there) and help keep a strong metabolism!
• Break down those carbs, proteins and fats into sugars, amino acids and fatty acids!
• Protect the brain and produce digestive enzymes!
• And give those cells a boost!

 TIMED TO PERFECTION!

Staying with the substitution analogy, it's no good one player coming on and trying to do his or her bit without knowing what the other ten team-mates on the pitch are doing and why.

'UNITY IS STRENGTH' reads one of the famous banners on the Kop at Anfield and nowhere is this more true than with micro-nutrients.

Together, vitamins and minerals act like all the moving parts of a watch mechanism within our bodies. Like clockwork, in other words.

A mineral such as iron, for example, has a very important function to do with our blood flow and energy levels, but we need enough Vitamin C to utilise the iron properly, so both are vital components of the 'mechanism'.

Size matters, too. The body needs both magnesium and selenium but more of the former and less of the latter, so we know which one would be represented by a bigger cog or wheel in our timepiece illustration...

IMMUNE TO ALL THAT...

There has never been a more important time to protect and strengthen our immune systems and vitamins and minerals play a crucial part in this. So much so that having a poor intake of micro-nutrients can often result in an increased risk of falling ill – particularly for footballers during periods of intense training or a congested fixture schedule. Put simply, good food choices reduce the risk of harm.

EAT A RAINBOW A DAY!

Nutrition is about more than just making sure we eat regularly, it's about enjoying as many different colours as possible on our plate. And although carbs, protein and fats contain micro-nutrients, it's fruits and vegetables that absolutely do the job!

The many colours of fruit and veg come from the various natural pigments they contain. One major group are called carotenoids and from these we get the red-orange pigment called beta-carotene and found in carrots, for example.

Another are phytonutrients, for example lycopene which gives tomatoes and watermelons their red colour, while allicin is an oily, light-coloured pigment that gives garlic its unique odour.

The wider the variety of colourful fruit and veg in each meal, the higher your micro-nutrients intake. It's simply the best way of getting the range of vitamins and minerals that your body needs to thrive. In other words, not only should that 'watch mechanism' look bright and beautiful, it will be benefiting our bodies too!

Leafy green vegetables such as kale and spinach are rich in an important mineral called magnesium, for example. Red apples or darker grapes are good for antioxidants (more about them later). Lighter-coloured vegetables like onions or kale are richer in vitamin C.

It's worth remembering too that nuts are rich in fat and protein but because they are plant-based they also have a very high micro-nutrients intake. The same for seeds and dried fruit.

So micro-nutrients are very famous for their colourful choice and they can be added to all sorts of meals. On our dinner plate we might have white or pale yellow potatoes, a red beef steak, or pink salmon, but it's the vegetables (and their micro-nutrients) which bring the extra colour.

For dessert it could be a cream-coloured rice pudding – why not jazz it up with colourful berries or cherries or even an apple mash?

And where and when possible, try to choose fruit and veg which is 'in season' – naturally available in this country at the time of the year.

VITAMINS & MINERALS MADE EASY

Vitamins and minerals are the substances and elements in foods that our bodies need to develop and function normally. They are both mostly known by one or two letters and these are just a very few examples.

FUNCTION / FOUND IN

FUNCTION / FOUND IN

VITAMIN A
Helps the body's natural defence against illness and infection – the immune system.
Cod liver oil, sweet potatoes, carrots, black-eyed peas, spinach, broccoli, red peppers.

ZINC
Promotes wound healing, creates DNA, keeps immune system strong.
Red meat, oysters, poultry, seafood, beans, nuts, whole grains.

VITAMIN K
A group of vitamins that helps wounds to heal and may also keep bones healthy.
Green leafy vegetables (broccoli,) spinach, cereal grains.

IRON
Helps carry oxygen throughout the body, essential for breathing and energy.
Lean meat, seafood, poultry, spinach, beans.

B VITAMINS
Required for energy metabolism and nerve function.
Whole grains, cereals, meats, leafy green vegetables.

MAGNESIUM
Involved in blood-sugar control and blood-pressure regulation.
Almonds, spinach, cashews, peanuts, black beans.

VITAMIN C
Essential for the growth and repair of tissue and may decrease cold symptoms.
Strawberries, oranges, peppers, grapefruits, kiwi, lemons.

CALCIUM
Aids muscle contraction, nerve signalling, bone growth and strength.
Yoghurt, cheese, milk, fortified orange juice, soy milk, tofu.

VITAMIN D
Promotes calcium absorption, aids in bone growth.
Salmon, tuna, milk, yoghurt.

SELENIUM
Acts as an antioxidant, protects the body from damage caused by infection.
Seafood, beef, poultry, wholewheat bread, eggs, milk.

VITAMIN E
Helps protect us against harmful 'free radicals' when fat is broken down.
Sunflower seeds, almonds, peanut butter.

POTASSIUM
Helps control the body's balance of fluids, helps the heart work properly.
Bananas, Brussels sprouts, beans and pulses, nuts and seeds.

THE GREATER OF VARIETY OF COLOURFUL FRUIT AND VEGETABLES, THE MORE VITAMINS AND MINERALS TO BOOST YOUR BODY'S PERFORMANCE

ANTIOXIDANTS EXPLAINED

———

'Antioxidant' is a general term for a substance which helps boost our immune system by preventing or delaying damage to the body's cells caused by unstable molecules called 'free radicals'.

These free radicals are produced by a chemical reaction called oxidation which happens when the body breaks down food or is exposed to tobacco smoke or radiation. So that's why they're called antioxidants.

According to FIFA, they are also important in helping to protect the body's tissues against the stresses of intense football training because they reduce muscle soreness and reduce inflammation.

Natural antioxidants include vitamins C and E, a mineral like selenium, and pigments (carotenoids) such as beta-carotene, lycopene and lutein.

The richest sources are fruits and vegetables, among them broccoli, spinach, carrots, potatoes, artichokes, asparagus, avocados, beetroot, radish, sweet potatoes, squash and pumpkin – and it all comes back to the choice of colours.

DON'T FORGET YOUR FIBRE!

———

Fibre is the name given to a range of substances found in the cell walls of vegetables, fruits, pulses and cereal grains.

Some fibre is soluble in water and some isn't. So as well as helping you feel full, which means you're less likely to eat too much, it can help other food and waste-products to move through the gut.

Potatoes are a good source of fibre when eaten with their skins on, along with wholegrain bread and wholegrain breakfast cereals, brown rice, and wholewheat pasta.

Some types of fibre in oats and pulses may help to reduce the amount of cholesterol in your blood.

It's GREAT to HYDRATE

GETTING INTO THE HABIT OF TAKING FLUID ONBOARD

A long with carbohydrates, proteins, fats, minerals and vitamins, there is a sixth subject to consider...hydration.

Because it's so simple and obvious, it's often overlooked and underestimated. But hydration is vitally important to how our bodies function – in fact we wouldn't survive without it. And if athletes don't hydrate properly, they simply cannot perform to their maximum or recover afterwards as quickly and fully as possible.

Everyone can experience dehydration and it occurs more rapidly after exercise or travel or when we're feeling under pressure or stressed. So whether you play football or not, it's good to get into the habit of drinking fluids like ordinary or flavoured water.

Clearly, hot weather causes us to lose more water from our bodies through sweating. But even if you're outside and it's cold, the environment can make you want to wee, which further increases the risk of dehydration!

So whatever the weather, and especially when you're training, it is essential to replace fluids lost. Drink regularly throughout the day and also during sessions. Come to training and matchday prepared and hydrated. Take advantage of drink-breaks according to the weather and intensity of the drills, and during a match use opportunities to drink like the warm-up and at half-time.

Better intake of fluid (and fuel) during a game can deter injury and cramp, which occurs when we're not properly hydrated and also when we lose too much sodium through our sweat.

Likewise it can keep us running further and faster as the match progresses and help us to maintain skills and judgement until the 90th minute and beyond. Think how many games are won and lost in those final moments.

Water as a source of hydration is a great choice at any time of the day because it doesn't add extra calories to our diet and it's obviously required for those vitamins which are soluble in water as oppose to fat. But don't forget you can find it in fruit and vegetables, too, like the cucumber, melon, zucchini and pumpkin. All those little cogs and wheels again, working together.

Above all, staying hydrated – especially if you're a footballer – is simply about being smart.

8 HYDRATING TIPS

1. Keep a reusable bottle or container for your water or flavoured drink and get into the habit of taking it everywhere with you.

2. Whenever you're travelling from A to B, think about W for water – whether it's in cars or on public transport we tend to dehydrate.

3. Try sipping water throughout the day rather than taking large gulps or drinking a bottle in one go.

4. Aim to drink around 2 litres of fluid per day – besides water, drinks such as milk, juices, tea and coffee (in moderation) are fine.

5. Make your own flavoured water combos – with, for example, eight sliced strawberries, a quarter of a cucumber and half a kiwi fruit.

6. Try dairy-free alternatives like almond, soy, rice and oat milks.

7. Stick to one smoothie or small glass of real fruit juice a day – you get the vitamins and minerals without too much natural sugar damaging teeth.

8. After training in the cold, sometimes a warm drink is more satisfying – try gently heating up some of your favourite drinks during winter.

COME ON YOU

REDS...
and
GREENS...
and
YELLOWS!

IF MICRO-NUTRIENTS COULD PLAY A BIG MATCH,
THESE WOULD BE TWO SENSATIONAL STARTING LINE-UPS
– WITH PLENTY OF SUPPORT FROM THE BENCH!

PINEAPPLE
A flamboyant and commanding presence, it's hard to beat its sweet-tasting combination of vitamin C and manganese, or its brilliant bromelain reserves.

BLUEBERRY
The little wonder with the massive fan club. Tasty and versatile, it is low in calories but brimming with fibre, vitamin C and vitamin K.

STRAWBERRY
Very easy on the eye and extremely good for our bodies, providing plenty of assists when it comes to vitamins, fibre and antioxidants.

AVOCADO
Its CV reads like a who's who of the good stuff: vitamins C, E, K and B6, magnesium, potassium, beta-carotene, omega-3 fatty acids...

APPLE
Whatever its colour, the humble apple is the gift that keeps on giving: fibre, protein, potassium, iron. Green ones have more vitamin A.

WATER MELON
Literally the team's water-carrier. It's exceptionally refreshing and packed with nutrients and antioxidants, and practically no calories.

ORANGE
Hugely popular and no wonder – behind that tangy taste is a reliable source of vitamin C, fibre, thiamine, folate, and antioxidants.

Fruit XI

BANANA
Good in the air, this fab food-snack contains essential nutrients and can benefit digestion. Easy to eat – just ask all those tennis stars eating them between games!

GRAPEFRUIT
Pulling a face just looking at this subtropical superstar? It may taste bitter but research suggests its folic acid keeps our brains in good shape.

GRAPE
Enjoying a purple patch with its fantastic distribution of health-benefiting flavonoids and anti-inflammatory phytonutrients.

MANGO
It might have inedible skin and be deceptively plump-looking, but this nutrient-rich tropical favourite is low in calories and high in fibre.

ON THE BENCH
—

Apricot, peach, cherry, pomegranate, raspberry, cranberry, lemon, papaya (the list really does go on)...

GARLIC
Allicin! Allicin! A versatile little performer, it's not to everyone's taste but can be relied upon to clean the arteries and lower the blood pressure.

YELLOW PEPPER
Slightly younger brother of the red pepper upfront, it's bursting with vitamin C and can also assist with niacin to keep skin nice and healthy.

CAULIFLOWER
How's this for low in calories yet high in vitamins? And did you know it contains some of almost every vitamin and mineral you need?

BEETROOT
A prolific provider of folate (vitamin B9) as well as fibre, manganese, iron and potassium, it's thought to increase exercise performance.

ASPARAGUS
Consistently good at delivering antioxidant nutrients including vitamin C and E and the minerals zinc, manganese and selenium.

KALE
This kid's got it all: vitamins A, K, C and B6, and minerals like manganese, calcium, copper, potassium and magnesium. Okay, who just shouted "Gareth!"

PEA
Don't let its diminutive size deceive you – this is one vitamin-packed little powerhouse. Also high in fibre and low in fat.

Veg XI

RED ONION
Eye-wateringly efficient operator who scores every time with antioxidants which fight inflammation and boost the immune system.

POTATO
Well-known for playing out of its skin but even more impressive with it on! Rich in plenty of the best vitamins, minerals and antioxidants.

CARROT
A vegetable veteran with superb vision, known for its crunching challenges and bags of beta-carotene, potassium and antioxidants.

RED PEPPER
Strikingly sweet sibling of our dynamic right-back, it positively peppers (sorry) the target when it comes to fibre, iron and folate, not forgetting vitamin C.

ON THE BENCH

Spinach, broccoli, cabbage, lettuce, radish, sweet potato, squash, pumpkin (and plenty more we could mention)...

PLAYS FOR BOTH SIDES

Due a technical dispute over whether it's a fruit or a vegetable, the mighty red tomato – normally one of the first names on the team-sheet and a proven performer with its potassium and vitamin C – had to sit this match out.

FINAL SCORE... TOGETHER STRONGER!

It's honours even after this colourful encounter between a fantastic fruit team and their versatile vegetable counterparts.

Both sides gave it everything and displayed some outstanding vitamins and minerals when it really mattered.

And with all those micro-nutrients working their magic in the body, things like muscle soreness and fatigue shouldn't be a problem so we can expect a strong and quick recovery.

All in all, absorbing stuff!

Shiso Purple cress Micro Herb Sage Sechuan cress Lepid cress Micro Herb Mi... a Koppert cress

YOU ARE WHAT

CHOOSING THE RIGHT FOOD IS A GREAT START, BUT FOR MAXIMUM BENEFIT YOU NEED THE BEST BALANCE OF PORTIONS AND PERFECT TIMING WHEN YOU CREATE YOUR OWN FOOD 'TURNTABLE'

YOU

EAT

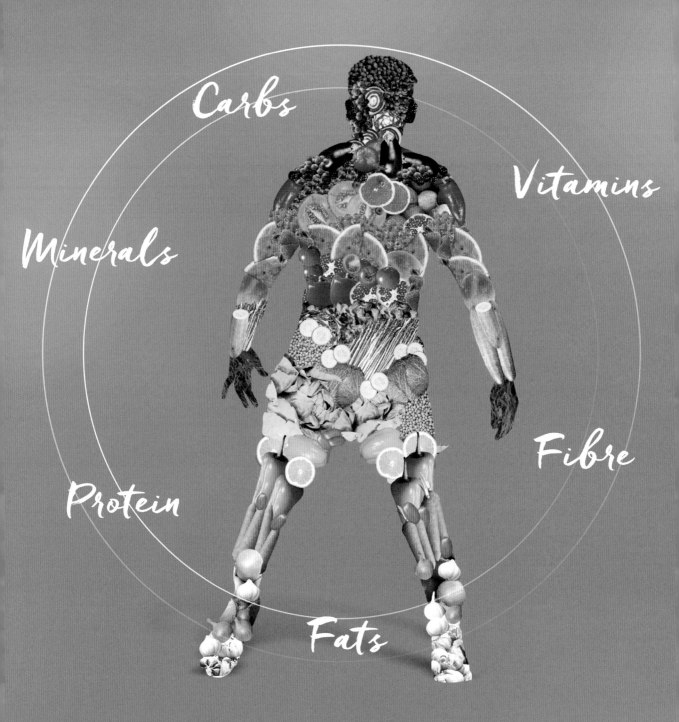

YOU ARE WHAT YOU EAT

Carbs

Vitamins

Minerals

Fibre

Protein

Fats

FUEL FOR PERFORMANCE

We've seen how different types of nutrients – large and small, and combined with physical activity – can benefit the body, and we've learned where they can be found. For a healthy lifestyle their many qualities are clear, but what about the actual quantities of carbs, protein, fats, fibre, minerals and vitamins?

Understanding and controlling your plate is crucial: how much of each nutrient source to have, and in which food combinations, depending on your daily and weekly schedules and your fitness and exercise regime.

So many factors can influence what a footballer should eat and when: everything from age and ethnicity to height and weight, metabolism and body-fat composition, allergies and intolerances, his/her position on the pitch and how often they play, the fixture schedule, their personalities, even the prevailing seasonal weather.

During a match, goalkeepers do not cover as much distance as, for example, full-backs. So it's simple maths that lithe, all-action players such as Trent Alexander-Arnold or Andy Robertson will need to take in enough carbohydrates before matchday to compensate for the calories they burn while playing – otherwise, their performance levels may not be as high.

FIFA's *Nutrition for Football* report (2005) revealed that top-class outfield players perform 'low-intensity activities' for 70 per cent of a football match as well as 150-250 'brief intense actions'. Overall they typically cover about 10-13 km around the pitch, of which 600 metres are sprinted and 2.4 km at 'high-intensity'.

Through the course of a game their heart-rate is around 85 per cent of the maximum rate and the oxygen demand is 70 per cent of the maximum oxygen uptake. All of this physical expenditure needs fuelling, and at LFC it's part of Mona's job to talk with each player and draw up their own individual diet recommendations. She also regularly consults the club's coaching, fitness and medical teams in order to make her assessments and adapt them for each player. And of course she works just as closely with the club chefs to source the best organic and preferably local food produce for the players.

85%

OF MAXIMUM HEART-RATE

Top-class outfield players can experience this during the course of a football match, as they perform up to 250 'brief intense actions' and also cover 10-13 km on the field.

CARBOHYDRATES

PROTEIN

FATS

FRUIT & VEG

PUTTING *it on a* PLATE

As we've seen, macro-nutrients (those three main energy-sources used by the body) and micro-nutrients (vitamins and minerals) have an important role in how the body functions as they help provide us with fuel, build muscle and repair damaged tissue, and generally keep us fit and healthy.

Later in this book there are some delicious, quick-and-easy recipes – look out for the symbols at the top of this page which will help you to understand the proportions of carbs and protein, for instance, on your plate.

To recap, carbohydrates are the primary source of fuel for footballers, so you need to 'top up' your stores by having more on your plate in the time leading up to training or playing. If you don't, you could end up being subbed before the game is over! By the same token, you shouldn't need a large amount of carbs at each and every meal or on a rest or recovery day.

To refuel properly, it's all about getting your carbs and protein in the right combination. According to FIFA, "during the 2-4 days prior to a competition, a player's need for [protein and fats] typically does not increase above the levels that are recommended for normal, moderate-level training."

So you don't necessarily require more protein before you play. But regularly-spaced meals throughout the day provide a 'pulse' of protein to boost muscle-growth and maximise recovery after training or playing.

Good carb sources include wholegrain bread and cereals, brown rice, wholewheat pasta, potatoes (with skins on) and dried fruit.

Good protein sources include lean meats like chicken and turkey, fish such as salmon, mackerel or tuna, and dairy products like milk, cheese and eggs.

You can also find protein in vegetables and non-meat sources such as beans, legumes and pulses, which provide other nutrients such as fibre. Basically, the wider the variety, the better.

Along with being a great source of protein, oily fish are also rich in omega-3 fats which can help lower blood-pressure and protect the heart. Studies also suggest they could improve a footballer's reaction-time and decision-making on the pitch.

Fruit and vegetables sometimes get overlooked by players of all ages, but they have so much benefit for your recovery, health and development. When you're making up your plate, try to include them first – things like salads and raw or cooked vegetables – and eat at least three servings of veggies per day and two portions of fruit.

Remember: it's quick and even more easy to chop up some carrot or celery sticks for your lunchbox and drop in a whole fruit like an apple or banana. For smoothies you can include green leaves such as spinach or kale and add one or two fruits to make a nutritious snack.

Some of our favourite dishes have 'secret veggies' in them. Take the sauce for spaghetti bolognese – most delicious when it consists of onion, celery, peppers, tomatoes and garlic, finely chopped and 'sweated' down in the pan until they reduce in size. It's similar to LFC's very own 'Lolo' or vegan bolognese – full of fabulous veggies!

Vitamin C can be found in high levels in both fruit and vegetables, for example citrus fruits, berries, peppers, sprouts and broccoli. It's a water-soluble vitamin – meaning it's circulated through the body but not stored – and a powerful antioxidant which helps to strengthen your body's natural defences.

Together with the mineral zinc, it's been shown to reduce the severity of cold symptoms (and so potentially allow you to continue to train) as well as repair bones, skin and cartilage (and so help to heal wounds or injuries).

Other micro-nutrients like B-vitamins, magnesium, iron, copper and fibre can be found in wholegrain cereals which keep you feeling fuller for longer and can help stop your body from absorbing bad cholesterol. They're called wholegrain because they contain the nutrient-packed 'bran' and 'germ' which are both removed in refined or processed grains.

SHOWING YOUR COLOURS

—

REMEMBER IN THE FIRST CHAPTER WHEN WE TALKED ABOUT
HAVING A RAINBOW ON YOUR PLATE? LOTS OF COLOURS IN YOUR
PORTION OF FRUIT AND VEG IS JUST AS BENEFICIAL AS HAVING
THE RIGHT AMOUNT – AND ALL OF THOSE COLOURS HAVE SHARED
AND INDIVIDUAL HEALTH BENEFITS

SHADES OF GLORY!

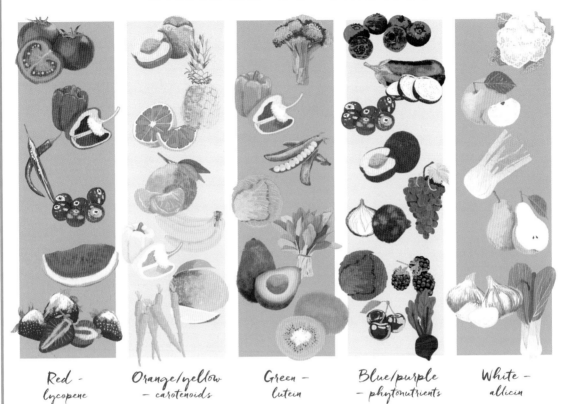

Red - lycopene

Orange/yellow – carotenoids

Green – lutein

Blue/purple – phytonutrients

White – allicin

Red – lycopene
Has been investigated for its anti-cancer properties, reduction in risk of cardiovascular disease and neuro-degenerative diseases such as Alzheimer's.

Orange/yellow – carotenoids
Rich in vitamin C which plays an important role in immune health and reducing muscle soreness, and beta-carotene which helps improve eyesight.

Green – lutein
Green vegetables are rich in lutein and vitamin K. These nutrients play an essential role in bone-health and also help support eye-health.

Blue/purple – phytonutrients
Blue and purple-coloured fruit and veg has a range of benefits and have been researched for their anti-ageing properties, because of the high levels of antioxidants found within them.

White – allicin
Lightly-coloured vegetables and fruits may not be as vibrant as others, but they contain powerful nutrients that can have a positive effect on cell-health and ageing.

A GUIDE TO PORTION SIZES

Many recipes traditionally have their ingredients measured out in amounts like teaspoons, tablespoons, cups and half-cups, pints (the old 'imperial' way of measuring volume) or litres (the metric equivalent), ounces/pounds (imperial weight) or grams/kilograms (metric).

It's fair to say, though, that most people probably don't think too much about portion sizes when eating. While scales and measuring jugs are very useful for cooking instructions, there is a handy method – literally – of measuring portion sizes for your plate. It's simple, quick and practical too.

While a 'pinch' of something like salt is self-explanatory, it's good to get into the habit of using a quick and easy portion-estimator. The hand graphics to the right are what the young players at Liverpool Football Club's Academy are taught.

There are five basic measuring amounts: two hands cupped together; a handful; a fist; finger and thumb (£1 coin sized); and a thumb.

THE 'MEALWATCH' METHOD

It's not easy for young footballers to manage their time around high-energy, nutrient-rich eating. 'Mealwatch' is a term used by Mona and her colleagues to help them organise and control their daily diets, creating periods for breakfast, lunch and dinner with occasional snacks in-between.

PORTION SIZES

Two Hands Cupped Together

A Handful

A Fist

Finger and Thumb
(£1 coin size)

A Thumb

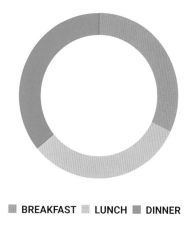

■ BREAKFAST ■ LUNCH ■ DINNER

■ BREAKFAST ■ LUNCH ■ SNACK
■ DINNER ■ SNACK

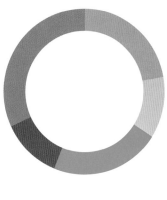

■ BREAKFAST ■ SNACK ■ LUNCH
■ SNACK ■ DINNER

A similar term to 'Mealwatch' is 'periodisation', simply structuring your eating habits around the requirements of training and playing.

At a club like Liverpool, the matches can come thick and fast: domestic league and cup ties, Europe and so forth. If the senior side is playing Saturday-Wednesday-Saturday, for example, there are hardly any 'recovery' days in that period. Sunday is a recovery day but then it's matchday minus 2 (Monday), matchday minus 1 (Tuesday), matchday (Wednesday), matchday plus 1 (Thursday), and then a similar pattern again.

Players constantly in the starting XI have a much higher need for carb-rich food for their refuelling process and to be organised and ready for the next game; whereas with injured players a lower-calorie regime might be necessary.

Portion sizes are not only a great way to get this balance right, they work well on the plate too – reducing the amount of carbs provides more space for something else, maybe another handful of steamed vegetables. And they can be adjusted periodically as each player's energy 'out-take' goes up or down.

So, the more physical activity, the greater the need for carbs – something like rice might take up half the plate, with the remainder divided between chicken (protein) and vegetables (vitamins and minerals). It's a bit like a 4-3-3 formation on the football pitch!

A moderate level of physical activity means a more even, three-way split on your plate between the rice, chicken and veg. Hardly any activity and the plate can be halved between the chicken and veg because there's less need for rice (carbs for fuel).

WEIGHING IT UP

Typical daily protein recommendations for the average population are 0.8 grams of protein per kilogram of body-weight.

That means a 70kg person should try to consume 56g of protein per day – roughly equivalent to a 200g chicken breast.

A UEFA study of nutrition in elite football found that top-level footballers have to consume more protein because of their increased physical activity – the demands of the sport require them to repair, maintain and sometimes build muscle-tissue.

For a non-vegan 70kg player, a typical day's protein-intake (in addition to sources of fruit, veg, carbs and fats) may be:
- *three eggs at breakfast*
- *one pot Greek yoghurt as a snack*
- *one chicken breast at lunch*
- *one handful of nuts after training*
- *one serving of salmon at dinner*

CARBOHYDRATE PERSONALISATION AND PERIODISATION

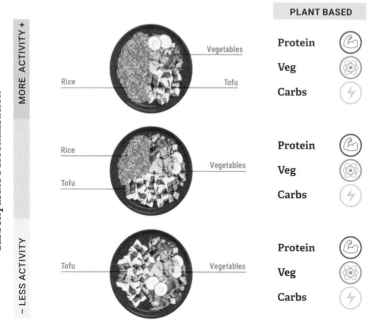

Carbohydrate Personalisation

MORE ACTIVITY +

– LESS ACTIVITY

MEAT OPTIONS		
Protein		
Veg		
Carbs		

Vegetables

Rice

Chicken

Protein		
Veg		
Carbs		

Rice

Vegetables

Chicken

Protein		
Veg		
Carbs		

Chicken

Vegetables

Example of how a plate can be personalised to a vegan option as well as being periodised by three activity intensities.

Carbohydrate Personalisation

MORE ACTIVITY +

– LESS ACTIVITY

PLANT BASED		
Protein		
Veg		
Carbs		

Vegetables

Rice

Tofu

Protein		
Veg		
Carbs		

Rice

Vegetables

Tofu

Protein		
Veg		
Carbs		

Tofu

Vegetables

To the left is an example of how a plate can be 'periodised' by three activity intensities – as well as being 'personalised' to a vegan option with tofu instead of chicken.

For young readers and developing footballers it's important to point out that these portion-estimators are just that: estimations. Precise numbers and percentages are all very well, but everybody is different and one size definitely does not fit all!

Neither do you have to be a footballer to periodise your plate. Whether you've cycled to your local grocers or farm to get some fresh fruit and veg, or simply sat back and enjoyed a bit of Netflix with a takeaway and a soft drink, you can adjust what goes on your plate next to restore the balance.

BREAK OUT THE LFC BUDDHA BOWL!

Buddha bowls are brilliant for Mealwatch because you can completely customise them to suits your needs and tastes. There's no healthier way to get a good balance of veggies, carbs, protein and healthy fats in your meal, and the concept has been adapted towards each player's needs at LFC.

There are a couple of different theories as to how this dish got its name: the first is from the bowl's big, round, Buddha belly-shape when filled; the other from presenting a meal where balance is a key Buddhist concept.

You can easily 'build' one by filling a third of the bowl with cooked meat or fish (or tofu) and adding one big handful of roasted or steamed vegetables (or both), some brown or white rice (or quinoa), some dressing (olive oil, lemon, fresh herbs or balsamic vinegar) and little extras like seeds or toasted nuts.

Try a combo of cooked and raw ingredients to create a more interesting meal!

MONA'S
Mealwatch

"Over the years we have developed a curriculum as a kind of five-year plan. So let's say there is a player in the LFC Under-12 team who might one day be in the U18s. In terms of education, what can we do to help this player to grow, to develop and be physically strong, to pick up good habits as they progress? And how do we work with the parents and 'co-create' with our local schools?

"We have a newsletter every month with different themes and infographics to make it more digestible for all age-groups. I'm a big fan of trying to explain things in a very practical, realistic way so people can understand immediately what they should aim to eat in their everyday lives.

"The idea behind 'Mealwatch' came over the years doing consultations with players. Food has a lot to do with logistics, and like everyone else players are living and working in real-time and have to plan their days and create routines around training sessions, kick-offs, meetings and other commitments.

"Professional players are really well-organised, especially because their itineraries are better-structured. But it's different for youngsters. They should never be on a diet or a low-carb regime or anything like that, but they can be well-prepared and organised.

"Let's say they go to school at eight, finish at four, sit in a vehicle for 90 minutes, train for 90 minutes, sit in a vehicle again for another 90 minutes... Even if they don't train on a professional level, they might do other things – go dancing, have a theatre group, anything. It's often the case that they are feeling a bit 'drained' in the evening. Maybe there wasn't enough hydration, maybe only one warm meal in school at midday.

"As a nutrition team, experience over the years has taught us that we needed to do something around timings for younger players. Mealwatch became a nice tool to explain things like the importance of having breakfast, maybe a snack at 10:30, staying fresh and concentrated during school lessons. Then they have their lunch, more lessons and maybe a snack before football training.

"So, breakfast, lunch and dinner, and the opportunity to add two snacks. Ideally

Mealwatch is based on the mechanism of a parking disc, with an arrow you can turn towards the different times of the day and different kinds of activities. For example, if you want to train at four o'clock, the Mealwatch says you should have your snack around a minimum of 90 minutes beforehand.

"Previously parents sometimes reported that their kids were without energy, tired and fatigued, so we'd check whether they'd had breakfast before leaving home, or if there was a snack in their lunchbox, or how far they had to travel – all these things. Now they and their children can use Mealwatch to check what they need.

"It's about making the right food-choice but it's also about wanting to be fit, awake, concentrated – wanting to feel like Jordan Henderson.

"You want to perform in school football or whenever you play. You don't want to get injured, you want to stay healthy and strong. You want to prepare yourself in the best way possible, to be always ready to perform at your highest level. That could be football or an exam at school – pass the exam, win the three points!

"Lastly I would never say that you should never have something like a takeaway delivery treat. It's more about how often you do it. You should never feel guilty – you should enjoy it, see it as something you've worked hard for, as long as you remember it's a special occasion and not part of your normal nutrition routine.

"Then you can look forwards and get your nutrition regime back to normal."

IT'S JUST A GUT FEELING

The global pandemic highlighted the benefits of a healthy immune-system – and it all starts in your stomach.

Did you know that over 100 trillion bacteria can be found in the gut? There are between 500 and 1,000 different types and they are involved in harvesting energy from food, balancing the good-versus-bad bacterial composition and manufacturing enzymes and vitamins.

The healthier your gut, according to some important studies, the better your quality of sleep. There is also an important link between your gut and your brain, which are connected by the body's nervous system – so it's true that feelings of fear, anxiety and even happiness might affect or influence your stomach.

Probiotics are a non-digestible food ingredient which stimulates the growth of beneficial micro-organisms in the intestines. Good sources include probiotic drinks, yoghurts and sourdough breads. The word comes from the Latin word 'pro' which means 'for' and the Greek 'biotic' meaning 'bios' or 'life'.

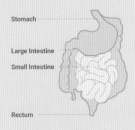

Stomach

Large Intestine

Small Intestine

Rectum

LINKED IN

The graphic above shows how the digestive system consists of the stomach and large and small intestines.

EAT, SLEEP, PLAY

Sleep can be recognised as one of the most critical aspects of a footballer's lifestyle. If you don't get enough good-quality sleep, it can affect your performance on the football pitch as well as your general wellbeing.

Studies have shown that a lack of sleep or disrupted sleep can increase stress hormones as well as the risk of contracting common colds. High-caffeine/sugar drinks don't help because they keep you alert, and neither do high-fat diets. But the right food intake, when it's well-planned, can play a vital role in enhancing sleep-quality and aiding rest and recovery.

While sufficient sleep and good food will help to boost your immune system, especially during the winter months, you'll miss fewer matches or training days due to illness if you:

• Practise good hygiene – wash your hands regularly with hot water and soap.
• Drink plenty throughout the day – hydration hydration hydration! Don't share water-bottles, keep yours clean.
• Try to avoid sick people – during hard training periods you are more susceptible to catching coughs, colds and sniffles.
• Don't miss meals, and cut out junk-foods wherever possible.
• Avoid 'crash-dieting' – when you're not eating enough calories it can lead to increased stress on the immune system.

REST ASSURED

Studies have shown that cherry juice may help improve sleep-time and quality. Cherries contain a compound called melatonin known as the 'sleep hormone'.

DIETARY REQUIREMENTS

Someone might decide to follow a plant-based diet because of their religious or ethical beliefs, or environmental concerns. There are also other special circumstances which cause athletes to change their dietary habits.

For example, Muslim players avoid food and fluid intake during daylight hours throughout the holy month of Ramadan – but again, performance will not necessarily suffer if the player is well-prepared.

PLANT BASED
Eating

Is it possible to become a top-level footballer if you don't eat meat? The answer is yes – with a little more planning and effort.

In fact there are many benefits to increasing plant-based sources of protein – such as lentils, beans, chickpeas, seeds, nuts, and meat substitutes like tofu and Quorn – even if you don't plan on becoming fully vegetarian. They all contribute to good health and wellbeing.

FIFA recommends that "players who avoid red meat must pay special attention to ensuring that their diet contains enough iron from plant sources, and this should be combined with other foods that aid iron-absorption, for example fortified breakfast cereals and glasses of orange-juice. Dairy products should be included in the diet to ensure an adequate calcium intake."

But even if you decide to stay plant-based, there is always a way.

Vegetarian: a person who does not eat meat or fish, and sometimes other animal products.
Vegan: includes the consumption of fruit and veg, legumes (beans, peas, lentils), grains, nuts and seeds; excludes meat, fish, poultry, dairy products and eggs.
Plant-based: foods derived from plants, including vegetables, whole grains, legumes, nuts, seeds and fruits, with few or no animal products.
Pescatarian: a person who eats fish and/or shellfish.

LFC UNDER LOCKDOWN

MONA EXPLAINS HOW TEAMWORK MAKES THE DREAM WORK!

"When this virus came up in early 2020, from a logistical point-of-view you try to think ahead as much as you can, so we kind of prepared for an eventual lockdown situation. Not that we wanted it to happen, but it's important that you have enough food and resources available, so we reached out to the suppliers early to discuss opportunities and how they saw the situation.

"When the actual lockdown started we'd all been to training, all been to work, in the morning and then went home at one o'clock for what was an unforeseen amount of time.

"We started to develop a creative and innovative solution adapted to the situation. We installed a delivery system to avoid the need for the players to go out, so they could follow the government regulations as much as possible by staying at home.

"It's not only from our perspective as a department, it's also all of our colleagues so it was nice to see how we were cooperating together, all communicating. For example, Andy Kornmayer and the fitness department delivered gym equipment to the houses of the players to extend the opportunities to still do exercise and workouts at home, and we tried to help from the food perspective.

"With regard to the delivery systems, the menu or recipe went out over WhatsApp or any digital channel and the players were able to write down what they needed if groceries were missing in the house.

"On the one hand it was keeping them all happy with what they were eating because you don't want bad-tasting food, especially at a time like that! On the other hand we didn't know how long we would have to deal with the situation, but obviously it was a fact that it would not just stop and everything go back to normal.

ROBBO: Fresh!

"It would be a big learning-curve to return back to training and a normal training routine. So we tried to help them to maintain their body composition and feed them food which was as nutritious as possible to support their immune systems because we knew that around this crisis, staying healthy was the main approach.

"We wrote 'sensible' menus for the players because difficult times can afford unusual or innovative approaches. We tried to adapt to the food situation, keeping it quite basic but still interesting and very tasty and, of course, all of what they needed because they were still working out and training.

"We had various situations: a few players living alone, a few of them had their families with them, a few were living in an area where they couldn't simply go to a supermarket to avoid any unnecessary contact. So we tried to be very sensible and do really, really good organisation around food-preparation to avoid any food-waste and all these things.

"As a team we continued working closely together. I missed the Melwood atmosphere, as it was. I missed the colleagues there and I was missing everything already after about two days! But how we set up the communication structure around us, connected us even closer in a way.

"We found a really good way to connect and share things and update each other with what was happening in all the different departments in the club. Everyone was working together, trying to prepare information and advice for the players, trying to keep the messages really smart, and it was lovely to see how wonderful the resources were in the club and how we were working together and staying strong in those very difficult and unusual times.

"Tom Maynard, our Academy performance nutritionist, did a fantastic job there: being in touch with the players, doing online cooking sessions with recipes and tips on how to avoid food-waste and what you can do with your leftover food, like dried bread and things like that.

"So we tried to proceed in our daily routine to support and help the players as much as we could, as creatively as possible. We have wonderful people at Anfield who were declared as key workers, helping with the deliveries.

"You never heard a 'no', it was always possible, there was always a way to make it happen and that was wonderful to see in such sad and difficult times. Teamwork really can make the dream work."

IT'S GOOD TO SHARE

There's a lot to be said for sitting down for a meal with friends and family – it's long been a tradition in countries like France, Italy, Spain and Brazil where communal dining is very much a social, 'soul-food' thing.

Good food goes perfectly with team spirit. Liverpool FC's players and coaching staff eat together before and after training at the AXA Training Centre in Kirkby, on the morning of a match at their hotel, and also after the game at Anfield in a special annexe next to the home dressing-room.

As well as getting all the right post-match nutrients to promote recovery, it's a chance to talk about the match, celebrate or commiserate – hopefully the former!

FOOD ALLERGIES *and* INTOLERANCE

A FOOD ALLERGY IS NOT THE SAME AS A FOOD INTOLERANCE. ALTHOUGH BOTH CAN BE CAUSED BY A NORMALLY HARMLESS FOOD, AN ALLERGY CAN BE POTENTIALLY LIFE-THREATENING BECAUSE IT OCCURS WHEN THERE IS A REACTION OF THE IMMUNE SYSTEM

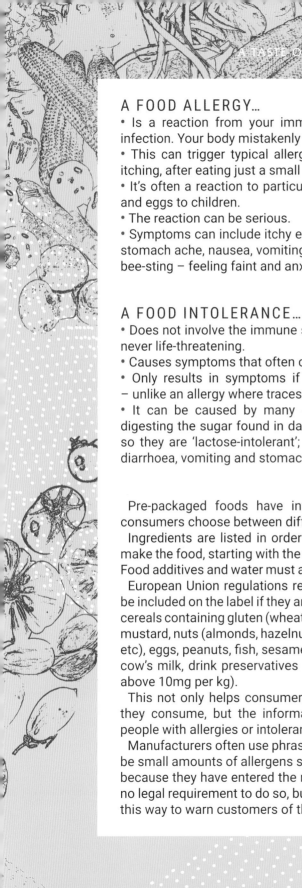

A FOOD ALLERGY…
• Is a reaction from your immune system – the body's defence against infection. Your body mistakenly treats proteins in foods as a threat.
• This can trigger typical allergic reactions such as a rash, wheezing and itching, after eating just a small amount of the food.
• It's often a reaction to particular foods – fish and nuts to adults, and milk and eggs to children.
• The reaction can be serious.
• Symptoms can include itchy eyes, dry mouth, red skin, shortness of breath, stomach ache, nausea, vomiting and diarrhoea, and anaphylaxis (similar to a bee-sting – feeling faint and anxious, hard to breathe, a fast heartbeat)

A FOOD INTOLERANCE…
• Does not involve the immune system – there is no allergic reaction and it's never life-threatening.
• Causes symptoms that often come on slowly, hours after eating the food.
• Only results in symptoms if you eat a reasonable amount of the food – unlike an allergy where traces can cause a reaction.
• It can be caused by many different foods. Some people have trouble digesting the sugar found in dairy products like milk, yoghurts and cheeses, so they are 'lactose-intolerant'; for others, wheat can cause bloating, wind, diarrhoea, vomiting and stomach ache after eating certain breads.

Pre-packaged foods have information on their labels which can help consumers choose between different foods, brands or flavours.

Ingredients are listed in order of weight relating to the quantities used to make the food, starting with the largest amount and ending with the smallest. Food additives and water must also be included if they are part of the product.

European Union regulations require that the following 14 ingredients must be included on the label if they are used in a pre-packed food: celery, molluscs, cereals containing gluten (wheat, barley, rye, oats), crustaceans (lobster, crab), mustard, nuts (almonds, hazelnuts, walnuts, cashews, pistachios, macadamia etc), eggs, peanuts, fish, sesame seeds, lupins (a kind of legume), soy beans, cow's milk, drink preservatives (like sulphur dioxide and sulphates at levels above 10mg per kg).

This not only helps consumers to understand more about the ingredients they consume, but the information also provides important guidance for people with allergies or intolerances who need to avoid certain food-types.

Manufacturers often use phrases like 'may contain' to show that there could be small amounts of allergens such as milk, eggs, nuts etc within the product because they have entered the manufacturing process accidentally. There is no legal requirement to do so, but many manufacturers label their products in this way to warn customers of the risk, no matter how small it might be.

FOOD FOR
All Seasons

HOW SPRING, SUMMER, AUTUMN AND WINTER AFFECT WHAT KINDS OF FOOD CAN BE GROWN IN A COUNTRY LIKE THE UK, AND AN EASY GUIDE TO THE DIFFERENT TYPES OF FRUIT AND VEGETABLES

These days we can easily take for granted what happens when we plant or sew a seed in the ground. Something actually grows from the earth. Not only that, much of it can be harvested, stored, prepared and eaten to sustain us as healthy human beings – a little miracle, when you think about it. But our knowledge of farming and agriculture has been gathered over thousands upon thousands of years.

In this chapter we look at the main edible plant types known as vegetables and fruit, along with cereal crops, rice, nuts and seeds. By and large, a fruit develops from the flower of a plant and contains seeds, while a plant's roots, stems and leaves are classified as vegetables.

Let's learn a little more about what they look like, where they come from, and how they grow and are harvested.

Planet
FOOTBALL

Recently it was a time like no other, with the 2020/21 football season starting and finishing later because of the global pandemic. But give or take a few weeks, the calendar has stayed the same: autumn start, spring finish.

The Premier League, like every other professional football league in the United Kingdom and most of Europe, traditionally starts in August and finishes in May – lasting around 10 months.

Ever wondered why? The obvious answer is that it's always been that way. In this country we're so used to experiencing the different 'meteorological' seasons on the pitch and inside the stadium in the following order: autumn with its matches played on light, mild evenings before the nights 'draw in'; winter with its drop in temperatures, gloves on the pitch, hats and scarves in the stands, the switch to yellow footballs and hectic festive fixture schedule; and finally spring with its title races, relegation battles, cup finals and the promise of summer holidays and international tournaments.

After all, British football just wouldn't be the same – nor would Liverpool FC's most famous anthem – without the storms, wind and rain!

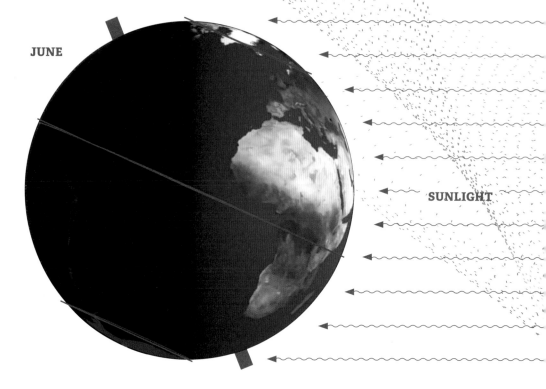

JUNE

SUNLIGHT

SEASONS IN THE SUN

So we know that our football calendar takes place over autumn, winter and spring – but why do we have the seasons we have? It's all to do with the way our 'pale blue dot' (as the famous astronomer Carl Sagan once described the Earth) orbits the Sun and the angle at which it does so.

We know that it takes our planet 24 hours to rotate completely on its own axis, and in that period we have daylight (the time when our part of the world is facing the Sun) and the darkness of night (the time when it isn't).

It takes 365 of these rotations for the Earth to complete one full orbit around the Sun, and all this time our planet is tilted on its axis by 23.5 degrees – so sunlight shines differently on us at different times of the year.

Where the British Isles is situated, in the planet's northern hemisphere, our winter occurs mainly in the months of December, January and February when the North Pole is tilted away from the Sun so its light strikes us at a shallow angle for a short period of time. That's basically why it starts to get darker during the second half of Saturday or Sunday-afternoon winter football matches.

In the same way it's the opposite in the summer when the North Pole is tilted towards the Sun so the light strikes us more directly for longer. Which is why those early-season 8pm kick-offs can often start without the floodlights switched on.

In spring and autumn, when the earth is tilted neither towards nor away from the Sun, the days and nights are more equal in length and we get something called the equinox – the point when the Sun is exactly above the Equator (the imaginary line around the middle of our planet). It comes from the Latins words *aequus* meaning 'equal' and *nox* meaning 'night'.

The most daylight occurs on what's called the summer solstice, from the

Latin *sol* for 'Sun' and *sistere* for 'stand still' – when the Sun appears at its highest in the sky. In the year 2022 it's Tuesday 21 June.

The least daylight occurs on the winter solstice – when the Sun seems at its lowest – which will be on Wednesday 21 December in 2022.

These things have been measured by humans for tens of thousands of years, helping them to plan when to plant, grow and harvest food-crops. It's thought that the prehistoric monument Stonehenge in Wiltshire (nearest football stadia, Swindon Town's County Ground and Southampton's St Mary's, for the record!) may have been built as a giant observatory for this purpose.

The brilliant British scientist Maggie Aderin-Pocock says that visiting places like Stonehenge makes her "think about our connection with the natural world" and "changes in season, weather patterns and the marking of time... intertwined with practical daily life." If you can't get there in person, English Heritage has a great website called Stonehenge Skyscape which lets you track the movements of the sun, moon, stars and planets 'live'.

Some people have even suggested that goalposts and crossbars look a bit like Stonehenge's huge upright and horizontal blocks, with the goalkeeper like a modern 'shaman' guarding the gates to the 'other world'. We couldn't possibly comment!

Lastly – and without wanting to complicate things – there are actually two different ways to calculate the seasons of the year: astronomical and meteorological.

The astronomical calendar is defined by what we've been talking about – the Earth's axis and orbit around the Sun – with the start-date of a new season falling on different days each year.

The meteorological calendar keeps it simpler, splitting the seasons into four periods of three months each – so weather-forecasters can compare seasonal and monthly statistics – with the seasons always beginning and ending at the same point on the calendar (give or take the odd leap-year day).

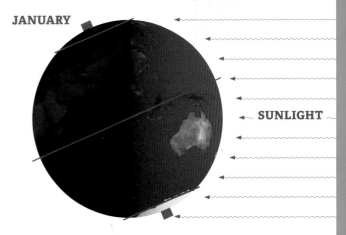

JANUARY

SUNLIGHT

ASTRONOMICAL V METEOROLOGICAL SEASONS FOR THE YEAR 2022

	Starts	Ends
Ast. Spring	20 March	21 June
Ast. Summer	21 June	23 Sept
Ast. Autumn	23 Sept	1 Dec
Ast. Winter	21 Dec	20 March (2023)
Met. Spring	1 March	31 May
Met. Summer	1 June	31 Aug
Met. Autumn	1 Sept	30 Nov
Met. Winter	1 Dec	28 Feb (2023)

GOALFESTS
AND HARVESTS

—

Although autumn is exciting for football fans because it signifies the start of a new season and perhaps the promise of silverware, in the farming world it symbolises a different kind of celebration and something far, far older: the time when crops are gathered or 'reaped' for food, known as 'harvest' after an Old English word (*haerfest*) for autumn. In Jürgen Klopp's home country Germany it's called *Ernte*.

It's been a tradition in Britain, like many other countries, to hold a 'harvest festival' (a bit like Thanksgiving in America) around the time of the 'harvest moon'. This is the full Moon nearest to the autumn equinox when the Sun is exactly above the Equator and the day-time and night-time are equal – for example Friday 23 September in the year 2022.

In the 'old days' a successful harvest could be the difference between prosperity or hardship and even life or death. An abundance of fresh, nutritious, locally-grown food could feed a whole community through the hard winter months before new crops were planted and seeds sewn the following year.

Harvest time became part of folklore and was (and still is) celebrated in things like music, painting and poetry – the "season of mists and mellow fruitfulness" as the Romantic poet John Keats described it in one of his famous odes.

It's also where we get the saying, 'you reap what you sow' – that is, you get out what you put into something. A good proverb for football, too.

Over the last 200 years or so, as more and more people moved from the countryside to towns and cities, it's fair to say we lost some of our connection with the natural world and our reliance on the seasons.

Today, over 83 per cent of us live in an urban environment. Anfield, for example, used to be a leafy suburb of Liverpool in the early 19th century. It's thought that under today's mighty Main Stand there was farmland belonging to two brothers who sold these 'fields of Anfield Road' to John Houlding, LFC's club's founder, in 1885. Who knows what kind of crops they might have grown there...

We still like to think we're in touch with nature. In a recent study of 2,000 adults in the UK, a whopping 86 per cent said they believed in the importance of seasonal produce, while 78 per cent claimed to shop for seasonal products – but only five per cent knew the time of year when blackberries were ripe and four per cent the best time to eat plums.

These days we're pretty spoilt with the availability of foods in supermarkets and local shops. This wasn't the case not so long ago, when foods were picked according to their seasonality and ripeness. Our great grandparents wouldn't have had strawberries around the table at Christmas, that's for sure!

Does it pay – in terms of nutrition and performance as well as cost – to shop according to the seasons? Well, when local produce is in season this usually means it will be less expensive, because the supply equals or exceeds the demand (and vice versa), and some people think it tastes better too.

These days we can get tomatoes, which are at their best from June to October, all year round. But foods can lose flavour and moisture as they are stored, transported and left on the supermarket shelves – how many times have you been shopping and found the last few pieces of forlorn-looking fruit or vegetables?

That said, if it's fresh don't be put off by 'wonky-looking' fruit and veg. Nothing is wrong with these apart from not having the desired shape or visual appeal, and some supermarkets have begun selling 'imperfect' fruit or veg at discounted prices.

Sometimes frozen produce can be a great alternative, sealing in flavour and locking in freshness. Using things like frozen berries and smoothie mixes are a good money-saving alternative to using fresh ingredients.

THE FOOTBALL SEASON IN FOOD

A (VERY) ROUGH GUIDE TO WHAT'S 'IN' WHEN IN THE UK. THIS IS ONLY A SAMPLE OF TRADITIONAL FRUIT, VEG, MEAT, POULTRY AND FISH, AND SOME OF THEM ARE AVAILABLE ALL YEAR ROUND!

AUTUMN

SEPTEMBER
OCTOBER
NOVEMBER

Matches on mild evenings, new signings settling in, European group games...

Carrots
Squash
Blackberries
Cranberries
Apples
Marrows
Cauliflower

WINTER

DECEMBER
JANUARY
FEBRUARY

Hectic fixture schedule, festive football, hats and scarves, yellow balls, FA Cup ties...

Sprouts
Potatoes
Cauliflower
Pears
Curly kale
Carrots

SPRING

MARCH
APRIL
MAY

Title races and relegation battles, Euro knockout rounds, League Cup & FA Cup finals...

Cucumber
Spinach
Apricots
Rhubarb
Cauliflower

SUMMER

JUNE
JULY
AUGUST

Close-season holidays, pre-season tours, friendlies, transfer gossip, here we go again...

Broad beans
Mange tout
Redcurrants
Cucumber
Strawberries
Blackcurrants

Celery

Sweetcorn

Onions

Ham

Dover sole

Plums

Garlic

Pork

Flounder

Venison

Lettuce

Chicken

Oysters

Pumpkins

Potatoes

Peppers

Red Cabbage

Mushrooms

Grouse

Skate

Parsnips

Swede

Turkey

Grey mullet

Pomegranates

Duck

Leeks

Turnips

Apples

Goose

Mussels

Artichoke

Cabbage

Chicken

Partridge

Scallops

Watercress

Carrots

Crab

Sea bass

Beef

Beetroot

Lamb

Trout

Haddock

Asparagus

Spring onions

Lobster

Mackerel

Gooseberries

Chicken

Salmon

Prawns

Runner beans

Courgettes

Ham

Crab

New potatoes

Watercress

Salmon

Radishes

Lamb

Beef

Apricots

Carrots

Chicken

Tomatoes

Beetroot

Mackerel

VEG IN SEASON

Asparagus SPRING
Bay leaves WINTER
Beetroot SUMMER
Broad beans SUMMER
Brussels sprouts WINTER
Cabbage WINTER
Carrots WINTER SPRING SUMMER
Cauliflower WINTER SPRING SUMMER
Celeriac WINTER SPRING
Celery SUMMER AUTUMN
Courgette SUMMER
Cucumber SPRING SUMMER
Curly kale WINTER SPRING
Fennel SUMMER
Garlic SUMMER
Green beans SUMMER
Leek WINTER
Lettuce and salad leaves
SPRING SUMMER AUTUMN
Marrow AUTUMN
Mushrooms AUTUMN
New potatoes SUMMER
Onions AUTUMN
Parsnips WINTER
Peas SUMMER
Peppers AUTUMN
Potatoes AUTUMN WINTER
Pumpkins AUTUMN
Purple sprouting broccoli SPRING
Radish SUMMER
Red cabbage WINTER
Rocket AUTUMN
Runner beans SUMMER
Sage SUMMER
Salad onions SUMMER
Savoy cabbage SPRING
Sorrel SPRING
Spinach SPRING
Spring greens SPRING
Spring onion SPRING
Squash SUMMER AUTUMN
Swede WINTER
Sweetcorn AUTUMN
Tomatoes SUMMER
Turnips WINTER
Watercress SPRING SUMMER

WHAT'S IN WHEN

These days plenty of food products are available all year round, but traditionally they tend to be at their best during one season and occasionally over two. It can be such fun buying or even harvesting fresh seasonal fruit and vegetables and discovering lots of new, delicious recipes to use them in.

AUTUMN

In the months of September, October and November, as the nights gradually get longer and the days get colder, hearty stews and warming soups are often on the menu. People also make their own jam from seasonal fruit like blackberries and plums.

This is the 'peak' time for apples, sweetcorn and marrow vegetables like pumpkins (for Hallowe'en, of course) and squash. Wild mushrooms are also in season – there are 15,000 species mostly growing in the UK's woodlands and meadows, but please be extremely careful because some are very poisonous.

Autumn and winter are 'game' seasons, too, when meat like venison (from deer) and grouse and partridge (birds) is popular, along with seafood such as oysters, Dover sole, flounder and skate.

WINTER

It's all about the root vegetables in Christmas and the new year, with turnips, parsnips and swedes perfect for the roasting dish – and the festive season wouldn't be the same for most people without Brussels sprouts.

Pears are a very popular fruit while leeks are a lovely ingredient for hearty stews and soups.

SPRING

While the football season reaches its finale, the soil is beginning to stir into life with the signs of fabulous fruit and veg like apricots, nectarines, gooseberries, spinach, cucumbers, spring onions and watercress.

April is rhubarb month! It's a plant which is classed as a vegetable, tastes like a fruit (the stalks) and can keep producing for a good ten years, and it's harvested in the UK at springtime.

So too is asparagus, and it's widely accepted that Britain has some of the best in the world. May is the month when it really comes into season.

Lamb is a particular favourite at this time of year, along with beef steaks and burgers, and (as always) chicken. But it's truly a seafood bonanza with crab, lobster, sea bass, haddock, mackerel, prawns, trout and salmon all in season.

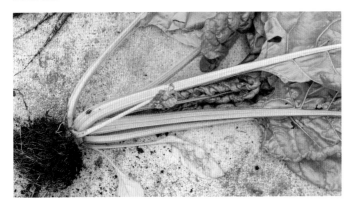

SUMMER

The National Trust website describes June as "a high point in UK gardens – the first spring-sown crops are finally ready to harvest and fruit bushes are dripping with jewels." Among them: strawberries, apricots, blackcurrants and redcurrants.

'Trending' in the vegetable garden are cucumbers, courgettes, carrots, watercress, radishes, beetroots, broad beans, runner beans, peas and mange tout along with tomatoes and those mouthwatering new potatoes.

Perfect for a refreshing seasonal salad and often accompanied by a choice of ham, beef, lamb, chicken, crab, salmon or pilchards.

FRUIT IN SEASON
Apples AUTUMN WINTER
Blackberries AUTUMN
Blueberries SUMMER
Cranberries AUTUMN
Currants SUMMER
Damsons AUTUMN
Elderberries SUMMER AUTUMN
Gooseberries SPRING
Greengages SUMMER
Loganberries SUMMER
Pears WINTER
Plums SUMMER AUTUMN
Quince WINTER
Raspberries SUMMER
Rhubarb SPRING
Sloes AUTUMN
Strawberries SUMMER
Tayberries SUMMER

BRING ON THE VEGGIES

Whole books have been written about vegetables and their various 'families', species and classes, many of which overlap, and it can all get a bit bewildering. We're going to keep it fairly simple by referring to the following types: leaf, flower, root, stem, bulb and fruit

WHAT LIES BENEATH...

Planted vegetables are like trees –
you only really see half the picture.
Above ground and visible to the eye
are stems, leaves, flowers, seeds, fruit
or pods; below the soil there may be
roots, tubers and bulbs.

Leaf

Leafy green vegetables are abundant, nutritious and tasty. They grow above ground and tend to have shallow root-systems.

Lettuce is a typical example and comes in lots of shapes and sizes, from the iceberg or crisp lettuce with its paler green leaves, to the darker romaine. Other leafy veg include spinach, Swiss chard, watercress and mustard greens, while several types are also classified as cruciferous (see next page), including cabbage, kale, rocket, collards.

High in minerals, vitamins and fibre and low in calories, they can be served fresh, steamed or stir-fried, drizzled with olive oil or balsamic vinegar, and flavoured with things like chilli flakes, sesame seeds or lemon.

FOOD IN FOCUS: SPINACH

Who's heard of Popeye the sailor? Before Spider-Man, Wonder Woman, Captain America and co, he was one of the very first animated superheroes and he got his super strength from eating spinach.

To this day there are statues of him in several American towns and cities where they just happen to produce... you've guessed it!

It might not give you the strength to hurl your arch-enemy to the moon (as Popeye did with Bluto) but spinach is most certainly a super food – its tasty, dark-green leaves are vitamin-rich and it's perfect for everything from salads to soups to curries.

Easy to grow at all times of the year, it naturally 'wilts' when cooked – so be sure to throw plenty into the pan. Its bittersweet taste goes perfectly with dishes like scrambled eggs and tomato on sourdough for a delicious, healthy breakfast or mid-morning brunch.

Celebrity chef Hugh Fearnley-Whittingstall says it "deserves a standing ovation for its contribution to quick meals – it's the leafy green that keeps on giving.

"Butter and cream are two of its best pals, but so are carbs such as spuds and pasta which soften its slightly metallic edge."

Flower ✱

These are vegetables which have flower petals shaped like a cross – hence their Latin name *cruciferous* (from which we get 'crucifix'). They are sometimes referred to as *brassica* which is Latin for 'cabbage'.

They include some of the world's most commonly-cultivated vegetables like broccoli, cauliflower, Brussels sprouts, bok choy, kale, collards, cabbage and radishes. They've attracted a lot of scientific interest for their reported cancer-fighting properties – among other things, they are thought to contain chemical compounds which could help protect cells from damage.

Either way, they are certainly part of a healthy, balanced diet.

FOOD IN FOCUS: KALE

If vegetables had their own social-media, kale would be trending. Cheap to buy, packed full of nutritional good stuff, and a versatile ingredient for all sorts of dishes, its arguably the coolest veg out there – and to think it used to be grown as cow fodder!

Kale looks a bit like cabbage but is better at braving harsh winters. Both its leaves and stems (chopped to stop them being too thick and tough) can be used in cuisine. The curly kale variety can be used to make pasta or pesto sauces with ingredients such as chilli flakes, garlic, parmesan cheese, anchovy fillets, salt, black pepper, olive oil and lemon juice. It's also great in stews.

With its absolute arsenal of vitamins and minerals, it's thought to tick all of these boxes: supporting the immune system; bone health; preventing heart disease; eye health; protection against cancer.

FOOD IN FOCUS: BRUSSELS SPROUTS

We're so used to seeing neat and tidy bags of sprouts on supermarket shelves but they look much more spectacular when still clustered along their long, thick stalks. They get their name from the capital of their country of origin, Belgium, where they were first cultivated.

The UK produces around 80,000 tons a year – enough to cover 3,200 football pitches – and demand for them at Christmas is so great that farmers work around the clock to harvest and pack them. Sprouts are high in fibre, low in calories and packed full of vitamins and minerals.

Because they have shallow roots, they can be top-heavy so their stalks are often supported in fields and gardens by wooden stakes. The whole stalks are harvested at first – they stay fresher longer that way. Then the sprouts are picked from the bottom upwards, with the smaller, tightly-leaved ones sharply snapped off, one by one. In the kitchen, once you've cleaned and trimmed them, try cutting a little cross symbol in their stems – they'll cook more evenly that way. Sprouts can be steamed but get a bad press when they're 'overdone'. Try roasting them for a crispier texture and nuttier flavour.

Stem

Often we don't take much notice of which actual parts of a vegetable we're eating, and it's amazing to think that shoots and stalks, just like leaves, flowers, roots and seeds, can be edible in some instances – like celery, fennel, asparagus and rhubarb.

Stems tend to be a plant's main part and they can have a very distinctive texture and flavour. Celery can be eaten raw while others are cooked before they are eaten.

They're full of vitamins, minerals and antioxidants and can be used in tasty recipes.

Formby Asparagus Trail

FOOD IN FOCUS: ASPARAGUS

The tender young stems of this extremely popular, early-summer delicacy are known as spears and these are the parts which are harvested in the UK's short but super asparagus season or 'window' from April to June.

Britain has some great local producers and not far from Anfield is the Formby Asparagus Trail where the crop was and still is grown among the sand dunes and exported around the world. Check out the giant wooden asparagus-themed sculptures as you follow the paths.

A great source of vitamin K, asparagus is best eaten freshly-cut but can be stored in the fridge for a few days. The spears are simply snapped with the top halves steamed or grilled, then enjoyed on their own or as part of other dishes. Try them with poached eggs – amazing!

Now and again you might see white asparagus, which is when the spears have been covered with soil to stop them turning purple then green in the sunlight.

In Germany, the home country of Mona and Reds boss Jürgen Klopp, a favourite dish is white asparagus with things like *schnitzel* (thin slices of meat fried in breadcrumbs), new potatoes and hollandaise sauce (made from eggs, butter and lemon juice) – not always super healthy but delicious and very famous in German cuisine.

Stem ◖◗

FOOD IN FOCUS: RHUBARB

Mmm, rhubarb… The very mention of the world triggers the tastebuds and gets us thinking about those sweet-tasting, pinky-green stalks, stewed or baked and served as a 'crumble' with custard or ice-cream or frozen yoghurt.

Hold on, though. TV chef James Martin says: "There is so much more you can do with rhubarb – it works well with sweet or savoury dishes and it's absolutely delicious with ginger or blood oranges!"

Rhubarb is one of those 'forgotten' favourites enjoying a renaissance in popularity thanks to the return to more seasonal eating. Botanically a vegetable rather than a fruit, it's what's called a 'hardy perennial' which means it can survive in the ground all year round, although it prefers open, sunny sites and can also be planted in very large pots.

In Germany there is an old saying that rhubarb should be harvested in months without an 'r' in their name – so May, June, July and August – when it is also safe for children to sit on the ground because the soil is warm.

These days, though, the season starts in April when the stalks can be gently pulled out of the ground by their base, taking care not to snap them. The Royal Horticultural Society advises growers not to harvest any in the first year after planting, and then to pick just a few each spring/summer 'so you don't over-harvest and weaken the plant'.

Rhubarb stalks are rich in antioxidants and some people believe that the redder they are, the sweeter they taste. But do not eat the leaves – they are poisonous.

Bulb 🧄

Bulb vegetables or alliums grow just below the surface. The bit you can see above-ground is the leafy shoot; the part underneath is the bulb, sometimes appearing in clusters and mostly used to enhance the flavour of dishes rather than be eaten on its own.

In onions, shallots and garlic, the good stuff nutritionally is in the bulb, and these alliums are well-known for their medicinal qualities – they are believed to prevent high blood-pressure and perhaps even cancer, and also help our nervous systems to work properly.

And who doesn't love peeling away the crisp outer layers of an onion like unwrapping a sweet, even though when sliced it releases a chemical called (wait for it) syn-Propanethial-S-oxide which can make us cry!

Other bulbs vegetables like chives and leeks are used in cooking more for their shoots, which can add something extra to lots of dishes.

ORGANIC LEEKS

FOOD IN FOCUS: LEEK

So maybe it was at the back of the queue when they were handing out the best vegetable names – more of that later – but what it lacks in glamour the leek more than makes up for in goodness.

A long and thick bulb vegetable which is in season from late summer through to winter, the leek is prized for its bundle of stem-like leaves or 'shanks' used for soups and stews, or steamed or stir-fried.

Originating in the eastern Mediterranean, it was probably introduced to Britain by the Romans and is today the national symbol of Wales.

There are leek-growing competitions all over the country and the current record is held by a gardener in Northumberland who recently grew a 'three-pot' leek measuring 572 cubic inches – that's about the size of the UEFA Champions League trophy!

The name 'leek'? It's an Old English word which has Saxon origins – in German it's *lauch* – and it's also where we get the word 'gar-lic' from.

Root

In this group we're including tubers too, which are similar but grow on a network of fibres which aren't part of the plant's root system.

Examples of root vegetables are carrots, parsnips (which actually comes from an Old French word for carrot), turnips, swede, radishes and beetroot (bit of a giveaway in the name of that last one). Tubers include potatoes, artichokes and yams. Sweet potatoes are a bit of both as they have 'tuberous roots'.

FOOD IN FOCUS: POTATO

At first glance the humble 'spud' may not be much to look at. But, as it says on the National Trust website, "unearthing a mass of perfectly-formed potatoes from the ground is one of life's greatest pleasures and something children never fail to find astonishing."

That, plus the fact that potatoes are so easy to grow and the promise of their tastebud-tingling flavour, means they'll always be the nation's favourite vegetable.

Boiled, baked, roasted, mashed, chipped…however you cook them you just can't go wrong. Check out the mouthwatering potato recipes on TV chef Clodagh McKenna's website, for example, to be blown away by their sheer versatility.

They've got the good stuff, too: carbs and fibre as well as vitamin C, vitamin B6, potassium and manganese.

Originally native to the Americas, there are now over 500 varieties in the UK alone. They are grown from specially-prepared 'seed' potatoes – known as tubers – with just one producing many potatoes to harvest. If you haven't got a field, a garden or access to an allotment, you can grow them in large pots, covered with compost, or even a 'plant-bag' on your balcony.

Spuds are perennial, meaning their growing cycle lasts for three or more years, and are classified as either 'earlies' or 'maincrops'. Early varieties are ready to harvest much sooner (June to August) and are what we call 'new potatoes' – with a firm, waxy texture, they don't store for very long so are best eaten fresh.

Maincrops stay in the ground longer and produce a larger harvest and bigger potatoes (late August through to October) which can be stored for longer too.

FOOD IN FOCUS: CARROT

Before we start, ever heard of 'The Bionic Carrot'? That was the affectionate nickname of David Fairclough, scorer of one of the most famous goals in Liverpool FC history – against St Etienne in the 1977 European Cup quarter-finals – on account of his distinctively-coloured hair as much as his spectacular interventions.

Carrots don't just come in orange – they can be yellow, white and purple too. They're not always long and thin, either (by the way, the world's longest carrot in 2007 was 5.8 metres – that's almost the length of the goalmouth in football). Some can be small and round.

But they're all quick and easy to grow, take up little space and are available all year round. And you can use them in everything from soups and slaws to cakes and jam.

They are also really good for us, indeed considered a 'superfood' due to their rich source of beta-carotene, vitamins and antioxidants which can help lower cholesterol levels and improved eye-health.

Today's garden carrots are a 'domesticated' form of a wild carrot native to Iran and Afghanistan. They've been in Britain since Elizabethan times and now apparently we eat around 10 billion of them a year!

Like potatoes they are often referred to as 'earlies' or 'maincrops'. It's usual to sew them in early summer – in an open, sunny site – and they'll be ready 12-16 weeks later.

UK garden writer and TV presenter Monty Don says you should 'thin out' the carrots soon after sewing – as in, gently pull some of them out of the soil by their stringy leaves – "so that the ones that are left behind are a decent size. If you have a mass growing together in a clump, they'll all be small. So if you want them to be a little bit bigger, you should give them a bit more room."

Try to buy locally-grown carrots that are loose rather than pre-packed – it cuts down on transport pollution as well as plastic usage. And for a bit of fun, chop off the top of one, leave it in a saucer of shallow water for a few days, then watch the little green leaves start to sprout!

CHIPS WITH EVERYTHING

—

Everyone loves traditional chips – the kind that go with battered fish and salt and vinegar, especially at the seaside – but there are so many other amazing alternatives to the deep-fried variety which uses potatoes.

On the snack shelves in shops and supermarkets you've probably seen packets of dried or 'dehydrated' root vegetables.

Better still, why not make an even healthier version at home by slicing them fresh, tossing them in olive oil and oven-baking until crisp? Flavoured with sea salt, pepper, paprika or other spices, and fab as part of a snack or eaten with fresh dips!

Follow a good, trustworthy recipe (preparing the ingredients properly) and you can easily do this with veggies like parsnips, kale, carrots, beetroot, sweet potato, butternut squash, courgettes, onions and many more (depending when some of them are in season).

And check out this book's recipes chapter for our Rainbow Veggies special!

Root

MONA ON SUPER SPUDS…

"Most people know that a potato grows underground, but it's great to learn more about them, especially because nowadays you go to the supermarket and you often only see them packed in plastic bags.

"They're easy to grow them – really easy. Anyone can grow them in a pot on a balcony, for example. Mums and dads know that when you buy a pack of potatoes, sometimes one gets left and goes a bit crinkly and then these little white things start to come out! They're actually the sprouts of the potatoes and when they're in that state, you simply put them in the soil.

"Potatoes react towards light, so you want to flatten the soil over them then create a little hill or mound. Out of one potato, eight, nine or ten will grow, so the volume under the soil will be much bigger – but we don't want the little spuds coming out of the soil and seeing daylight because that's when they turn green and that's when you can't eat them anymore. A substance called solanine is created which is not good for us at all. Avoid at all costs!

"The potato family is big. Along with the many regional varieties, there are sweet potatoes which are very on-trend, and also blue or truffle potatoes – they're really nice and violet-coloured.

"Once you've harvested your spuds, whichever kind they are, it's about how you cook them – what I call 'product knowledge'. As I mentioned at the start of the book, if you fry one it can taste nice but the nutritional value is lost.

"I really like new potatoes with a little bit of sea salt or maybe potato salad with some chopped, fresh cucumber added. It has quite a liquid consistency but doesn't run on the plate. Very German but so versatile to add in your menus and the players love it.

"Baked or jacket potatoes are also nice for cooking with kids – you can flavour them with different types of herbs and dips for a quick and easy meal. Nutritious, too, and the wonderful things is that potatoes are naturally gluten-free. They are alkalic as well, which is really good for us because most of the world nowadays eats too much acidity.

"In the winter months you can always do a Sunday dinner with roast potatoes without too much fat by using a 'coated' pan or by drizzling oil over them from a vessel with a stopper – that way, you have a bit more control. Another nice thing, before the potatoes go in the pan or on the tray, is to marinate them in a bowl, again using much less oil.

"But hey, when it comes to Christmas Dinner, it's really alright to go with your favourite way!"

Fruit 🍎

Vegetables called fruits? It's simply because they contain seeds and develop from the flower-producing part of a plant, which in botanical terms is what fruit does – as opposed to 'normal' veggies which are the edible part of plants, like leaves, flowers, stems, roots, tubers and bulbs.

They come in many shapes and sizes, including marrow, squash, pumpkin, cucumber, aubergine, courgette, melon, avocado and tomato, and they can be harvested in summer (the ones with softer, edible skins) or stored through winter (thicker-skinned varieties). But many of them, wonderfully, possess the same kind of teardrop-shaped seed.

FOOD IN FOCUS: PUMPKIN

We're more used to seeing them carved into scary faces and lit-up for Hallowe'en, but pumpkins have a distinctive flavour too and are great when roasted or used to make soups or stews.

These large, round, orange varieties of squash are easy to grow – they like a warm, bright place and plenty of water. After harvesting, if left to 'cure' or harden in the sun they should keep for about six months. They are an excellent source of potassium, vitamin A and beta-carotene.

Why not grow your own next time for Hallowe'en and see if you can beat the current UK record for the biggest pumpkin, weighing in at over 1,500 pounds in October 2020 and so big it needed to be hoisted by a tractor.

That's heavier than seven Virgil van Dijks!

Learn about Legumes

When is a vegetable not strictly a vegetable? When it's a legume, a rich source of fibre, beneficial fats and minerals, and more closely related to seeds. Examples include green peas, broad beans, beans, chickpeas, peanuts and lentils.

FOOD IN FOCUS: PEAS

Peas are simply a British institution – they just seem to go with everything! You can grow them in pods on a vine indoors or outdoors as long as they have a little sun – on a balcony or window ledge, for example, or in an allotment, with a little support such as netting or twigs – and they look great too.

They come in three main types: 'shelling' peas (just the peas are eaten); sugar snaps (where you can eat the whole 'pod' with the peas inside); and mange touts (flat pods with tiny peas inside). The last two are the easiest to grow and tend to taste the sweetest.

Peas are sown from seeds in spring and picked in the summer, and of course they can be frozen to enjoy all year round. Websites like the Royal Horticultural Society and Gardeners World are great for showing you how to grow them, step-by-step.

Studies show that peas may help improve our blood-sugar balance and heart health, and among the other benefits are their richness in fibre and micro-nutrients.

FOOD IN FOCUS: CHICKPEAS

Chickpeas are rich in protein, naturally gluten-free and also deliver several types of micronutrients. They've been cultivated and used in cooking for millennia, with their origins in the Middle East, the Mediterranean and India. Today, among other recipes, they're mashed to make a delicious dip called hummus or street food like panelle, a fritter famous in Sicily.

Inexpensive and versatile, they are usually bought in tins, pre-cooked and packed together, pale and 'waxed'. But they're often darker and sometimes green when they grow in clusters of up to three inside 'pods' with spiky ends, and there are larger varieties too. You should never eat them raw – if bought dried, they have to be soaked in water overnight.

TYPES OF PEAS

Shelling or garden peas – plump and firm when removed from the pod for cooking.

Mange touts or snow peas – flat pods with very small peas inside, eaten together.

Sugar snaps – edible peas and pod, so-called because they snap when bent.

BEST FRUIT FORWARD

Just like vegetables, there are a few different categories of fruit: apples and pears, citrus, stone fruit, tropical and exotic, berries, and melons

Apples and Pears

"Autumn seemed to arrive suddenly that year," writes JK Rowling in *Harry Potter And The Deathly Hallows*. "The morning of the first September was crisp and golden as an apple…"

While apples are traditionally associated with autumn and the time of harvest, pears are usually picked later in the year, right through to December. Generally-speaking, both are fruits which have a 'core' of small seeds, surrounded by a thick, edible layer of 'flesh'.

FOOD IN FOCUS: APPLES

Money might not grow on trees, but apples do – and quite easily too. There are thousands of different types but they broadly fall into two categories: 'dessert' apples for eating, and 'cookers', as the name suggests, for cooking.

The old proverb 'An apple a day keeps the doctor away' isn't strictly true – it should be part of a wider variety of fresh fruit and veg in your diet – but it does help in terms of fibre and vitamin C.

At Liverpool FC's AXA Training Centre, box-fresh apples are always on offer in the canteen, but they can also be used in desserts like crumbles and savoury dishes.

They can be crisp or soft when bitten into, sweet or tart to the taste, and be streaked or blushed in colour with 'rust' patches.

But as well tasting so good, there's something else about apples that makes them so special to us. For centuries they were 'part of the landscape'. They connected us – and still do – to our childhoods and a 'lost time'.

Orchards, the groves or areas of land where apples trees are cultivated, also provide vital habitats for wildlife such as woodpeckers, bees, bats and moths. But in Britain their number has declined by 90 per cent since the 1950s.

These days the National Trust manages many historic orchards and helps to conserve ancient 'heritage' apple varieties with fabulous names like Ashmead's Kernel, Winter Queening, Coer de Boeuf, and Flower of Kent – this last one inspired the scientist Isaac Newton's theory of gravity.

Anyone lucky enough to have an apple tree in a garden will know how wonderful its blossom looks in spring. When the apples are ripe and ready to be harvested in autumn, some will already have fallen to the ground (called 'windfalls') and the others can be picked by cupping each one in your hand and gently lifting it off the branch.

Citrus

"Oranges and lemons, say the bells of St Clement's" is the first line of a well-known nursery rhyme from medieval times when ships used to offload Spanish oranges at markets along London's bridges.

But this group, which also includes limes and grapefruit, can actually be traced back to three 'ancestral' fruits: the mandarin from China, the pomelo from Malaysia, and the citron – a big, yellow variety – from India.

During the Renaissance, citrus fruit was so highly-prized in Italy that it was displayed not just in gardens but in great piles on tables at banquets, and rich people even commissioned paintings of it. Later it became valuable to the British navy as a cure for scurvy, a disease in sailors resulting from a lack of vitamin C.

Today in Britain we spend £750m annually in our supermarkets on citrus, which equates to 400m kilos eaten every year – mostly imported from Spain and South Africa. But it can also be grown in pots outdoors in summer and inside for winter.

Michael Barker, the editor of *Fresh Produce Journal*, says "the modern British consumer wants things now which can be eaten 'on the go' and that's meant a big rise in the sales of 'easy-peelers' like satsumas and mandarins.

"We're also seeing a real trend for people buying citrus for ingredients – you could call it 'the Great British Bake-Off effect'! And people want to juice more."

The BBC Sounds *Food Programme* calls citrus "a family of fruit that raises the spirits with its smell as well as its taste, and adds all kinds of 'zing' to cooking… They can bring swagger and freshness to drinks, transform a stew, lift a rushed home-cooked meal, [and] make a dessert that sings!"

FOOD IN FOCUS: LEMON

"Lemons are the best flavour companion in the kitchen – they go with everything," says one foodie article on *The Guardian* website.

"They can get a bit overlooked as they are so commonplace and cheap, but they have so much hidden value [and] every part can be used: the zest [bright yellow skin], oil, pips, juice, the insides. They are such a valuable ingredient."

Lemons have a high vitamin C content which, as we have seen, can shorten the duration of common-cold symptoms and even halve the risk if you're taken regular intense exercise like playing in a football match.

They are packed with potassium, so drinking the occasional glass of water in the morning with a slice of lemon is a really good start to getting your daily dose of this essential mineral.

Lemon skin or peel, which consists of the outer zest and the inner pith, contains valuable antioxidants, too. Unwaxed lemons with thicker, knobbly skin are the ones to buy for this.

Lemons with smoother, thinner skin are good for juicing. Leave them at room temperature then firmly roll them back and forth on a work surface under your palm to break down the flesh's fibre and extract the maximum amount of juice.

A fresh lemon wedge is wonderful as a side dish for grilled fish, or use half a lemon to stuff a chicken before roasting.

Tropical and Exotic

In recent years climate change has seen a few exotic types of fruit cultivated in more temperate climates, but as a rule tropical favourites such as bananas, mangoes and pineapples are still predominantly grown in the world's southern hemisphere and exported to countries like the UK.

Growing in bunches of five to 20 'fingers', bananas are picked when two-thirds ripe and slowly convert their starch into sugars as they're shipped.

Ripe Thai mangoes have a mainly yellow skin with sweet, succulent flesh inside, while Brazilian varieties have a green and red skin. South American guava are green and yellow on the outside with a salmon-coloured interior.

Smaller tropical fruit include the kiwi fruit (fuzzy brown skin and green flesh), lychee (thin pink shell covering white juicy flesh), and passion fruit (purple shell and yellow pulp inside).

Take extra care when buying tropical fruit by checking it is plump, fresh-looking and feels heavy for its size. And once it's cut, it should be covered and refrigerated.

FOOD IN FOCUS: PINEAPPLES

These days you can buy pineapples in pretty much any supermarket but they were once a symbol for opulence and wealth – if you ever wander around Liverpool's Victorian-era streets you'll see carvings of them on some of the grander-looking buildings and statues.

The explorer Christopher Columbus is credited with first bringing it to Europe when he found the spiky-skinned fruit on the island of Guadeloupe in 1493.

There are few fruit as delicious or distinctive-looking as the pineapple. It's what's known as a 'compound fruit', consisting of a central stem from which grow dozens of individual flowers which fuse into a single fruit capped with a 'crown' sporting short leaves.

One serving of pineapple can provide more than half a day's recommended intake of vitamin C.

Tropical 🍍 and Exotic

MONA ON THE 'TROPHY FRUIT'

"We have pineapples not only on the menu at the AXA Training Centre in Kirkby but we also integrate them into specific shakes where we can. Here it's more of a snack, or part of a smoothie, but in Asian cuisine it's used as an ingredient in sweet-and-sour dishes.

"In supermarkets you often see rings or slices of pineapple in tins of little plastic trays, but I love the fact that the whole fruit looks so incredibly different from anything else.

"We kind of assume that they hang high up from trees, like coconuts, but actually they grow close to the ground. In fact you need a pineapple to grow a pineapple – from its leafy head placed straight into the ground, rather than seeds.

"It looks like a little yucca palm and it just comes out of the soil, up to 40cm in height, and the pineapple sits on top like a trophy! Then comes the hard work at harvest, cutting them clear of their stems with machetes or sharp knives.

"The pineapple is a juicy fruit but not as juicy as an apple or pear, for example. A lot of the pineapple juice in supermarkets is often a natural concentrate with added water and sugar – we call it 'nectar' as it's not 100 per cent freshly-squeezed juice.

"One of the wonderful things about the pineapple is that it carries an enzyme which is especially good for anti-swelling, and it's called bromelain. The funny thing is, it's mainly found in the stem which we normally cut away because it's quite 'woody'.

"The papaya fruit has a similar substance called papain, and together these two help to transport out liquid which you don't want in your joints after injuries or bruises. So there is a health benefit, along with the fruit's high vitamin C content."

Berries

This should be really straightforward, right? Anything with 'berry' in its name must be – surely – a berry? Not quite.

Nutrient-packed examples such as strawberries, blueberries, gooseberries and elderberries all fit the bill. But raspberries and blackberries, despite their name, are botanically more like stone fruit because each of their little juicy blobs contains 'drupelets' or tiny pits which get stuck in your teeth. Despite the category confusion, they are great fun to pick from autumn hedgerows, armed with a basket – particularly blackberries which are the fruit of bramble bushes – but please take care with any traffic on those narrow roads. And be extra-cautious about any wild berries you don't recognise – they can be poisonous.

FOOD IN FOCUS: GOOSEBERRIES

It may seem strange to focus on a fruit which has gone 'out of fashion' in the UK, but gooseberries have a fascinating back-story.

With their distinctive football-pitch green colour, these tangy little fruits were very popular in the first half of the last century. There were even country songs written about them in America.

But growing them takes a lot of tender loving care – not always possible on a large commercial scale – so you don't often see them on supermarket shelves alongside the more popular blueberries and raspberries. But look out for them in organic grocery and farm stores.

Low in calories and packed with nutrients and fibre (like most berries), when fully ripened they're soft, sweet and perfect for crumbles, pies, sorbets, jam and even drinks – mixed with elderflower, for example, in a refreshing cordial.

To this day people grow their own gooseberries and enter them in World Cup-like competitions, especially in northern England. Just recently a new record was set for the heaviest-ever gooseberry, weighing in at nearly 65 grams (around half that of a cricket ball).

Those old country songs we mentioned? Here's one for the Kop to adapt: *"Oh how I love gooseberry pie says I, How I love gooseberry pie, Since the time of the Flood, there's been nothing so good, So luscious as gooseberry pie!"*

FOOD IN FOCUS: STRAWBERRIES

No summer quite feels complete without eating strawberries and cream outdoors at some point. The good news is that strawberries are incredibly easy to grow with their plants able to prosper almost anywhere – in garden borders, containers or hanging baskets, although often with a little netting to keep hungry birds and squirrels away!

Strawberries are an excellent source of vitamin C, manganese and potassium. They are rich in antioxidants and plant compounds, too, which may have benefits for heart health and blood-sugar control. Seven strawberries make up a portion of one of your recommended 'five-a-day'.

If you don't grow your own, you can always go strawberry-picking – something of a British institution, with countryside signs aplenty inviting people to do just that. But the Royal Horticultural Society advises that they be eaten as soon as possible as they do not keep well once ripened.

Melon

The melon family can be subdivided into the pale and dark-green streaked watermelon, the orange-fleshed cantaloupe (also known as rock or sweet melon) and the wonderfully-named honeydew.

They are similar to vegetables like squash, pumpkin and cucumber in that they contain those familiar teardrop-shaped seeds. On a hot summer's day, there's nothing quite as refreshing as slice of sweet, cold melon.

FOOD IN FOCUS: PAPAYA

The papaya, also known as a paw-paw, is a melon-like tropical fruit which comes from Central America.

It's higher in vitamin C – very good for the body's immune-system – than the melon and has a juicy, peach-like taste. There are claims too that its antioxidants can help to maintain eye-health by reducing the degeneration of the retina.

Unlike the pineapple, this fruit grows from a tall trunk – sometimes up to nine metres (30ft) high – with a crown of leaves at the top, similar in appearance to a palm tree.

Ripened at room temperature, it can be eaten raw on its own – you cut the papaya in half lengthways and scoop away the seeds – or added to other dishes. Try chopping it with chillies in a salsa.

THE TROUBLE WITH TOMATOES

It's one of those predictive questions which pop up when you Google tomatoes – are they fruit or vegetables? It's the same story with peppers. Both contain seeds like some fruit and can be eaten raw. But because of their sweet-but-savoury taste, nutritionists consider both to be vegetables.

We've only had tomatoes in northern Europe since the 19th century when they arrived from countries like Spain, having originated in South America.

Today there are thousands of varieties and four main types which can be grown by anyone: cherry (smallest and often sweetest); salad (for light, summer dishes); beefsteak (big, meaty and great for grilling); and plum (ideal for sun-drying).

Anyone can grow smaller tomatoes at home with just a little time and space. It's fun and very rewarding to sew the seeds indoors then watch the tomatoes grow outdoors in pots or hanging baskets or a greenhouse.

What's more, it's pretty much guaranteed that your tomatoes – grown by you, watered by you, cared for by you, and picked by you – will smell just amazing and taste simply delicious when they've ripened in the sun.

CEREAL WINNERS

Ever walked or cycled in the countryside, or just peered out of a train window, on a summer's day and wondered what's growing in some of those sun-dappled or breeze-blown fields?

Chances are, it's a cereal crop like wheat, barley, rye or oats, all of which are cultivated primarily for their edible, nutrient-packed seeds.

Wheat is the world's most cultivated cereal, milled and turned into flour for the bread and pastry industries and all sorts of other foods.

It comes in 'hard' and 'soft' and 'red' and 'white' types and also varieties called durum and spelt. When ready for harvesting it has a golden-brown colour and is similar-looking to barley but with a shorter 'beard' – the bristly bit protecting the seeds, which come in triplets.

Barley is more yellow-white in colour and its longer, bendier beard (protecting single seeds) can make a whole field look fuzzy. It's an important grain for the production of alcoholic

Corn grows as 'cobs' or 'husks'

Wheat has a distinctive 'beard'

Barley is more bendy

Rye has a slender appearance

Oats grow in 'panicles'

beverages like beer and whisky, as well as being used animal feed or 'fodder'.

Rye looks very much like barley but tends to be longer and more slender. With its seeds that come in pairs, it's used for making bread, beer and animal fodder.

Oats are a bit different from the above three. They don't grow in spikes but in what are called panicles, and neither do they contain gluten – the protein which triggers an immune reaction in some people. So they can be enjoyed as part of a gluten-free diet.

They're a hardy cereal (able to grow in poor soil conditions) and their high nutritional value makes them popular for things like breakfast cereals, muesli and cereal bars.

When crops like wheat and barley are harvested, their leftover stalks are gathered in bales and dried to become straw. In turn this can be used as bedding for animals or for making baskets and hats, or even as a fuel source for bioenergy. Hay is dried grass stored and used to feed livestock (farm animals) in winter months or times of drought.

Corn is another cereal crop which grows as 'cobs' in leafy 'husks' – if you buy them in this state from a farm or grocers, rather than wrapped in plastic at the supermarket, they tend to keep fresher for longer.

Enjoyed by Native Americans for centuries, sweetcorn is eaten when it's young and sweet – and delicious straight from the pan – whereas the maize variety is left to mature and become starchy so that its kernels can be ground into flour.

WHY RICE IS SO NICE

Not native to this country, rice is actually a grain – the seed of a type of grass mainly grown in flooded 'paddy fields' – and one of the most important sources of carbohydrates on the planet. Like oats, it's naturally gluten-free. Although it is imported from many other countries worldwide – with 50,000 varieties and rising – it can be stored because it's a 'dry good'.

In the kitchen it may be quite a simple food cooked with water, but it's never ever dull! That's because you can do so many things with it, using different kinds and combinations in salads, side-dishes, stir-fries and main meals. No wonder it's frequently on the menu at the AXA Training Centre in Kirkby where Mona and her team have created a 'portfolio' of rice and alternatives like amaranth, quinoa and buckwheat.

In the takeaways in the streets around the

stadium at Anfield on matchdays, the rice is usually white. But most rice is naturally brown after harvesting. This is the high-fibre, high-nutrition wholegrain, and once this outer layer is removed or 'husked, the remainder is white.

In terms of length and shape, rice can be long grain, medium grain, and short grain. Its texture ranges from sticky or light and fluffy, and some varieties give off fragrances while being cooked.

Arborio rice is grown mostly in the north of Italy and used to make risotto, while bomba or calasparra is famous in the Valencia region of Spain and traditionally added to paellas.

Basmati is an elegant, long-grain rice originally from the Himalayas and found in many Indian restaurants. Jasmine is a fragrant favourite native to Thailand. Sushi rice meanwhile is the short grain speciality of Japan.

Elsewhere you can find black rice (very nutritious but takes longer to cook), brown rice (another wholegrain type and very filling), and wild rice (originally from North America with a rich, nutty taste).

KNOW YOUR NUTS

Edible nuts have become part of many people's diets because of their health benefits – lowering levels of 'bad' cholesterol and reducing heart disease, for example – and they are often consumed as high-protein, gluten-free snacks between main meals. And of course they can be stored too.

The most popular types grown in the UK are hazelnuts, sweet chestnuts and walnuts, all of them delicious. Hazelnuts grow in small clusters on the tree of the same name and in late summer it's often a race between humans and animals to see who can pick them first!

Never confuse sweet chestnuts with horse chestnuts or 'conkers' – the former are covered with a fine, green and prickly coat, whereas the latter have a smooth outer layer with spines and cannot be eaten! Sweet chestnuts are virtually fat-free and rich in fibre.

Hazelnuts grow in small clusters

Sweet chestnuts have fine, prickly coats

It's a squirrel thing

Wrinkly walnuts are easy to recognise!

Walnuts are one of Nature's true works of art. Inside each hard, wrinkly shell is the kernel or 'meat', usually made up of two halves separated by a partition. The ones you see in packets have been artificially dried to keep longer.

Walnuts are so crammed with goodness that there is even an annual conference about them at the University of California to discuss the latest research. They are proven to be rich in antioxidants and omega-3 fats, and may help with brain function, low blood-pressure, weight control, a healthy gut and even healthy ageing.

Popular non-native nuts include almonds, pistachios, cashews, Brazil nuts and Macadamia nuts, while peanuts are classified as legumes.

As well as a big value in terms of micronutrients, nuts contain what we can call 'good' fats, from which we get things like peanut butter or almond oil. As always, it's about having a sensible intake, and try not to eat too many salted nuts – they may be tasty but there are no real health benefits.

Often on the menu at the AXA Training Centre is a snack based around nuts which many of the players love. A roll of parchment paper is layered over a baking tray, to which walnuts or hazelnuts or almonds are added, and then a sprinkle of maple syrup, before it's popped into the oven for 15 minutes at around 180 degrees.

When you take the tray out, sprinkle a little sea salt over the nuts then let them cool. It has a caramelisation effect – without using too much sugar – and the sea salt makes the taste 'explode'! Have it with some fruit like a banana, have it on its own – either way it's delicious!

And check out our Sweet 'N' Salty Nuts recipe later in this book!

TOP SEEDS

Linseeds are great providers of fibre

Edible seeds can come from cereals, legumes and nuts, all of which we also talk about in this chapter, as well as other plant sources – and these include linseeds, sesame seeds, pumpkin seeds, sunflower seeds, poppy seeds, vanilla seeds and pomegranate seeds.

Popular seed recipes include breakfast bars and 'energy balls'. They also add an extra dimension to salads and a crispy coating to meat, fish or tofu. They're easy to store in the cupboard too because they don't take up much room, but you could easily compile a whole book about them.

Just recently on the BBC Food website there was an article entitled 'The Nutrition Powerhouse We Should Eat More Of'. It described seeds as a family which supported the heart, bones, muscles, brain and immune-system.

Liverpool FC (ENG)

Sunflower seeds come from the big, beautiful flower

Linseed comes from a flowering plant known as flax, which is also cultivated for its oil and a fibre made into linen (from which bedsheets and some clothes are produced).

These small, reddish-brown or golden-yellow seeds can be eaten whole or ground. Because they add so much fibre to your diet, you should add them sparingly to breakfasts, salads, stews or even desserts. Soak them first, too, because their edges can be very sharp.

Next time you carve up your own pumpkin for Hallowe'en, collect the seeds, clean and dry them out. Flat, oval and greenish, they are delicious roasted or toasted. Or you can store them in a jar and around May the following year put them in some soil and start growing your own pumpkins!

They are also rich in protein, iron and phosphorus, as well as zinc which develops natural 'killer cells' which help to fight off viruses.

Sesame seeds, which are great added to stir-fries and even cookies, contain copper which helps to fuel immune cells and folate which can assist with producing new cells.

Sunflower seeds come from the big plant of the same name which belongs to the daisy family. They can be whole and dark-coloured or 'de-shelled' and lighter, and they are a source of protein, iron, calcium, potassium and phosphorus. They can also be roasted (shells on or off) for an on-the-go treat. They are known as *pipas* in Spain and South American countries where they are eaten as a snack in football stadiums.

Whichever seeds you prefer, there is the added joy of planting some of them – in a window-sill pot, garden or allotment – to see if you can create new life.

HYDRATION

Drinking enough water each day is crucial:
- to regulate body temp
- Keep joints lubricated
- Prevent infections
- Deliver nutrients to cells & keep organs

MICRO HERB
Nutrient Shot
Iron copper zinc
Magnesium
Anti Oxidant

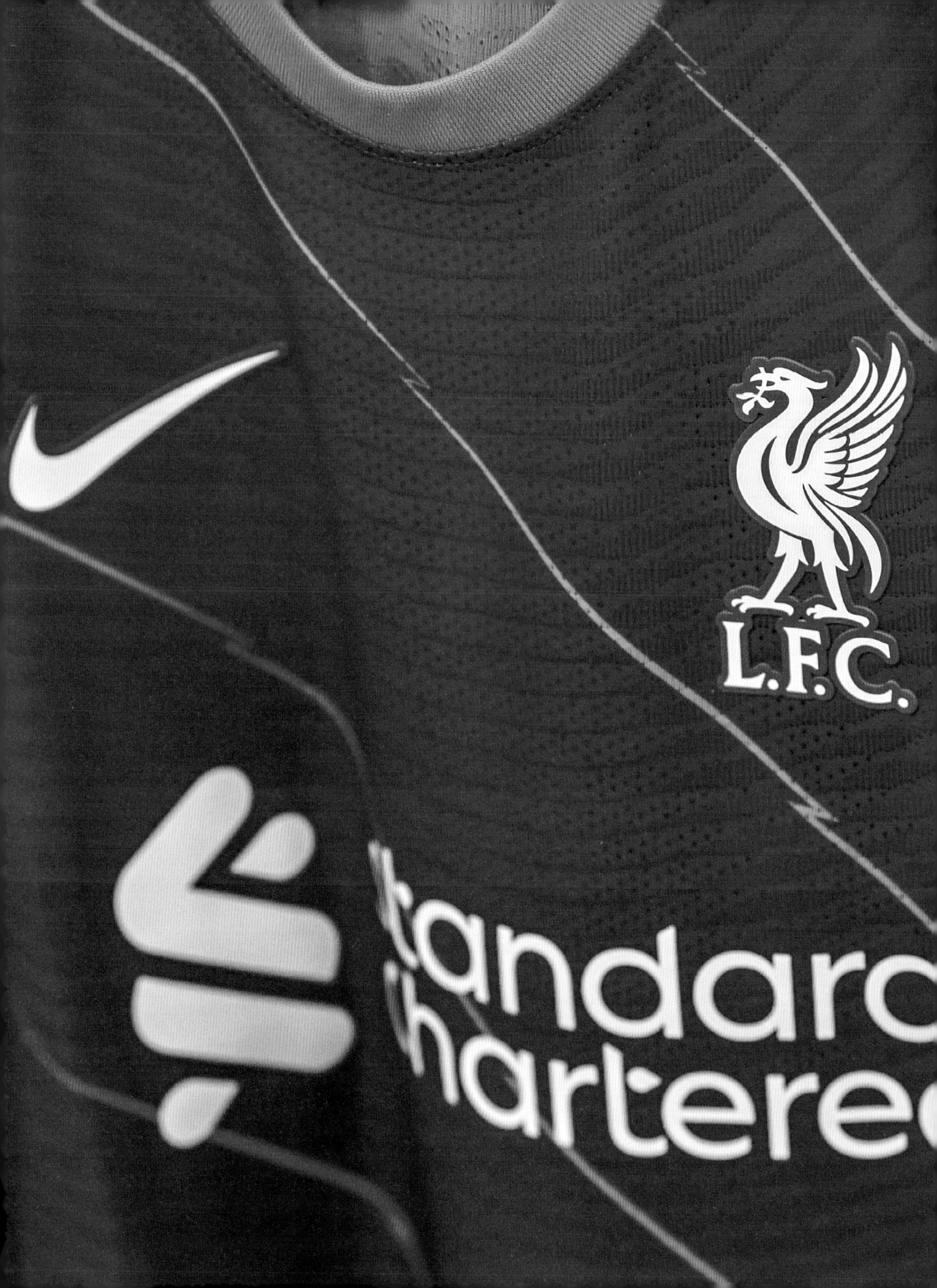
L.F.C.

The WORLD in ONE CLUB

—

WHAT DO PEOPLE LOVE TO EAT IN BRAZIL AND JAPAN? WHAT DO THEY MOSTLY GROW IN THE MIDDLE EAST? AND WHICH LIVERPOOL PLAYERS LIKE COOKING? ALL IS ABOUT TO BE REVEALED

Jürgen Klopp has always said that the more local-born players in his first-team squad, the better – as long as they are good enough.

Sure enough, in the Premier League title-winning season of 2019/20, among the leading six clubs only Tottenham Hotspur fielded English players more often than Liverpool – accounting for just over 37 per cent of total minutes played compared to just under 35 per cent for the Reds.

Among those English players at Anfield: Jordan Henderson, James Milner, Trent Alexander-Arnold, Joe Gomez, Alex Oxlade-Chamberlain and Curtis Jones.

LFC's second most-used nationality was Brazilian: goalkeeper Alisson, midfielder Fabinho and attacker Roberto Firmino.

Then there were the players from Europe like Virgil van Dijk and Gini Wijnaldum (Netherlands), Joel Matip (Germany), Divock Origi (Belgium) and Xherdan Shaqiri (Switzerland).

And then those born and brought-up on other continents who'd also played in Europe: Mo Salah (Egypt, Switzerland and Italy), Sadio Mane (Senegal, France and Switzerland), Naby Keita (Guinea, France, Austria and Germany) and Takumi Minamino (Japan and Austria).

Season 2020/21 saw the additions of Greek defender Kostas Tsimikas, Portuguese striker Diogo Jota, and Thiago Alcantara – a Spanish international born in Italy to Brazilian parents, who'd also played in Germany!

That's quite a mix, and with all those different backgrounds and cultures it makes for a fascinating exploration of the world's food too.

FOODS AND NATIONAL DISHES FROM AROUND THE WORLD

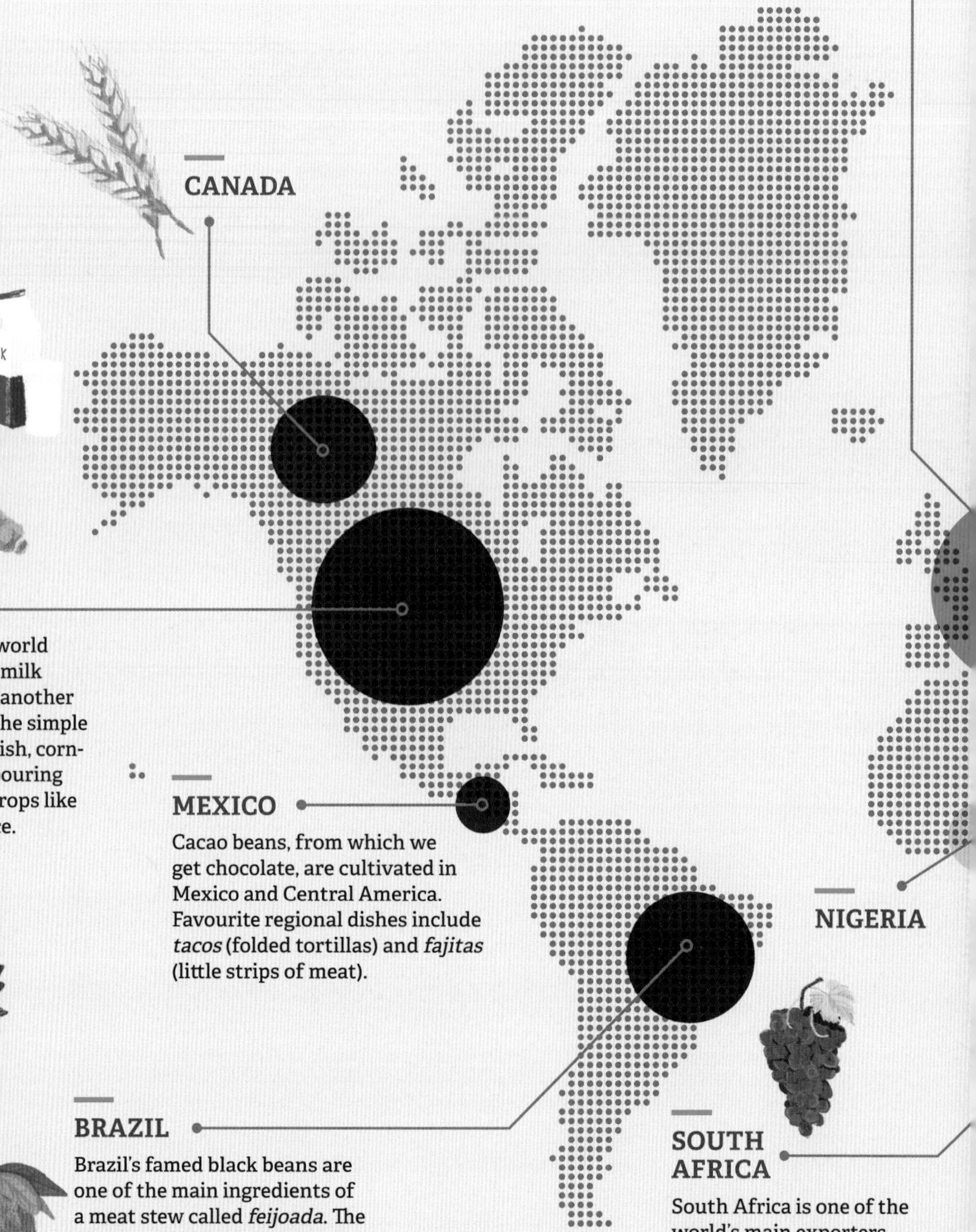

CANADA

USA

The USA leads the world in producing dairy milk while sweetcorn is another speciality – hence the simple and very popular dish, corn-on-the-cob. Neighbouring Canada produces crops like wheat in abundance.

MEXICO

Cacao beans, from which we get chocolate, are cultivated in Mexico and Central America. Favourite regional dishes include *tacos* (folded tortillas) and *fajitas* (little strips of meat).

NIGERIA

BRAZIL

Brazil's famed black beans are one of the main ingredients of a meat stew called *feijoada*. The country also exports chicken, beef (as does Argentina), rice, coffee and oranges.

SOUTH AFRICA

South Africa is one of the world's main exporters of sugar cane and grapes, but one of its favourite dishes is 'Bunny Chow' – simply hollowed-out bread with curry.

EUROPE

Every nation in Europe has its own beloved foods and dishes. Spain is the home of *tapas* (small, tasty dishes), *jamon* (dry-cured ham) and *paella* (made with rice and often seafood). Italy gave the world pasta and pizza plus some of the finest wines. Its ice-cream (dairy-based) and sorbet (frozen fruit-juice) are much-loved too. Both countries produce olives, as do other Mediterranean countries like Greece, Turkey and Morocco.

RUSSIA

Russia is a major producer of potatoes, and this vast country is also ideal for growing oats, barley and wheat. Nearby Uzbekistan is known for its carrot production, behind only China.

CHINA

China is the leader in production of many foodstuffs including rice, tomatoes, watermelons, strawberries, onions, cabbages and cucumber. 'Peking Duck' is a traditional dish, while nearby Korea has *kimchi* consisting of fermented vegetables.

JAPAN

Japan is the home of succulent *wagyu* beef and super healthy *sushi* – raw fish with rice. All the way across the Pacific Ocean in Peru is the favourite *ceviche* – raw fish again but with lime juice.

VIETNAM

Thai and South East Asian dishes are popular all over the world, from noodles and satays to curries and soups like Viet Nam's fabulous *pho*.

AUSTRALIA

Australia is second only to the United States of America in producing almonds, while nearby New Zealand is famous for its lamb.

MIDDLE EAST

The Middle East is the home of *hummus* and *falafel*, the famous dip and deep-fried balls made with chickpeas, plus *shish kebabs*.

EAST AFRICA

East African countries such as Kenya, Tanzania and Ethiopia produce many vegetables, for example runner beans and sweet potatoes. Further west in Nigeria a popular dish is *jollof* rice made with goat meat.

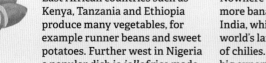

INDIA

Nowhere produces more bananas than India, which is also the world's largest exporter of chilies. Rice, another big export, is a staple of many delicious recipes.

NEW ZEALAND

I MAKE SURE I EAT AND DRINK THE RIGHT THINGS

—

REDS DEFENDER VIRGIL VAN DIJK ON HIS FAVOURITE FOOD, COOKING SKILLS AND DEBT TO MONA AND HER TEAM

Virgil, what is the most popular dish in your home country?
In terms of traditional Dutch food that is very popular I would say *Boerenkool* which is mashed kale and potatoes mixed with sausage and gravy. It's quite nice.

When you were growing up as a kid, was there a favourite meal that the family all enjoyed?
When I grew up there was always loads of rice and veggies and beans. It was just a question of what would be with the rice – sometimes chicken, sometimes beef or turkey. There was a strong Surinamese influence with my mum and so there was a lot of rice around.

And in terms of a food product did you have a 'guilty pleasure'?
There is a picture of me as a kid at McDonald's with some chicken nuggets and I think like most young kids I used to like going there with my mates. But to be honest, I didn't go that often.
  I don't really think I had a guilty pleasure. Like most young kids I used to enjoy eating sweets and candy but, again, I didn't eat that much. We didn't have a lot of money to eat out in the first place so we used to eat what we had.

What is your favourite meal after training at Kirkby and why do you like it?

As the years go by you appreciate more that certain veggies and drinks can help you stay fit and recover better.

I think with experience my decisions on what to eat are more guided by how hard the [training] session is going to be. After a tough session I might want to have more carbs and proteins. The main aim is to stay as fit as possible.

I love food to be 'honest' and I love pasta, sushi, beef and chicken. I like a bit of everything really. But at the training-ground, the decision is always guided by the sessions that you have coming up or that you have just completed.

And what is your favourite meal at home and why do you like it?

I can't cook myself so I'm really blessed that my wife is a fantastic cook. I would probably say something like pasta or a nice chicken salad as I really enjoy them. As a Dutchman I also love fresh breads and certain cheeses. Although it is not the most fat-free or carb-free, I do enjoy some cheese from time to time.

For breakfast: baked eggs, omelette, porridge, or protein pot?

I don't eat very much in the mornings as I don't really feel that hungry at that time of the day. I usually have scrambled eggs either with salmon or just plain with some green or red peppers and some water. I never drink tea or coffee in the morning.

What is your favourite fruit and veg?

I love fresh watermelon and also strawberries and kiwi fruit. For veggies, I love broccoli and also carrots and spinach.

As a cook, how would you rate yourself between 1 and 5 (with 5 the highest score)?

About minus 10! I think that you have to have a passion for it. I think you have to really enjoy preparing the food and I don't have that passion, to be honest.

As I say, I am really lucky that my wife is a fantastic cook, but on a scale of one to five I have to be truthful and say one.

If you could choose one team-mate to be your 'cooking buddy' who would it be and why?
Last season I would've said Gini Wijnaldum. He paid a lot of attention when he was younger and his grandma was cooking. Unfortunately I didn't pay as much attention. But we're from similar backgrounds and have that Surinamese influence, so I think Gini would have been a good choice.

Since you have been with LFC, what is the most important thing you have learned about good food and the right nutrition?
Since I first came to the UK it has been something that I have been increasingly aware of and now I pay attention to make sure that I eat and drink the right things.
 I speak to Mona a lot because she's been incredible for us and I want to make sure that I am doing all I can in terms of nutrition so that I can be performing at my best level.

During the day, how do you try to stay hydrated?
Just water. Gini used to call me 'Aquaman' because I only drink water and it's all I have in the house. Every now and again, I will enjoy a glass of wine with my wife.
 I don't really like fizzy drinks and don't like my kids drinking them so it's usually water.

Have you ever tried 'Scouse' and what did you think?
I've never tried it. I've seen it in the canteen at the training ground on quite a few occasions, but to be honest there have always been other options that have looked more appealing to me. Maybe I will try it one day, though!

In your opinion, what is the best smell in a kitchen or canteen?
Just the smells of freshly-cooked food. We are very lucky because the chefs at the training-ground work really hard and look after us all so well. They do an absolutely incredible job.

What has been the funniest situation in the canteen?
I can think of one. We once lost a game of five-a-side and as a 'punishment' we had to make a carrot cake. As I have said I am the worst cook so that was pretty funny although with the help of my team-mates it actually turned out alright in the end.

The club looked after all the players really well during the national lockdown last year...
I've said it many times to the chefs and to Mona that I don't think any other club looks after the players in quite the same way. Not only in terms of the deliveries of food and water that were made to all the players but also in regard to the variety of the food. You could tell it was all put together by people who really enjoy what they do and are passionate about their work.
 We all really appreciate the job that Mona and the chefs do for us and they have all played a big part in our successes.

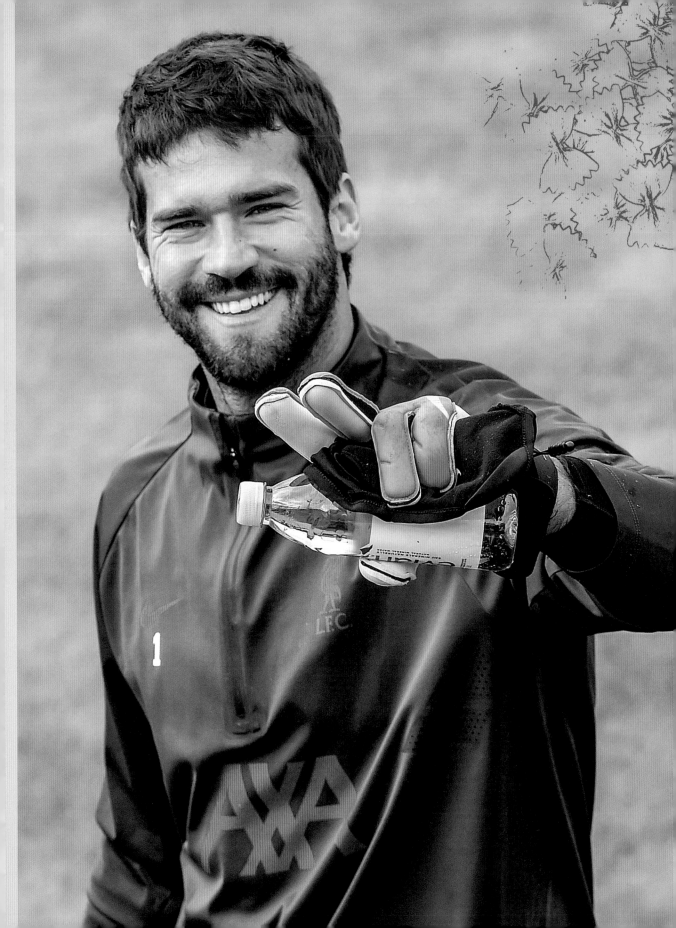

ALL ROUND TO ALI'S

**A QUICK-FIRE QUESTIONNAIRE WITH
THE GUARDIAN OF THE LIVERPOOL GOAL**

Most popular dish in your home country: Rice and beans with meat.
Favourite family meal when you were growing up: Breaded steak with a potato salad.
Favourite meal after training at Kirkby: Pasta.
Favourite meal at home: Rice and beans with meat, or a barbecue.
Breakfast choice: Omelette.
Dessert choice: Cheesecake.
Favourite fruit and veg: Mango and strawberries, and broccoli.
As a cook how would you rate yourself between 1 and 5? Four.
One team-mate as your 'cooking buddy': I would choose Bobby [Firmino].
Most important thing about the right nutrition: How it can help with the recovery between games, give me a healthy life and also help to improve my performance.
Staying hydrated: I drink water regularly throughout the day.

ADRIAN

I LOVE THE FAMOUS AXA LFC LASAGNE

GOALKEEPER ADRIAN, WHOSE PARENTS WORKED AS GREENGROCERS, GIVES US A TASTE OF HIS HOME COUNTRY OF SPAIN

Adrian, what is the most popular dish in your home country?
Food is an obsession in Spain and we are lucky enough to have a very wide variety of recipes. But I think *paella* is the dish with the most international recognition of the Spanish gastronomy around the world.

The main ingredients of *paella* are rice, vegetables and a selection of meat, fish and shellfish. However, forget the *chorizo* and chicken *paella* – it does not exist in Spain!

When you were growing up as a kid, was there a favourite meal that the family all enjoyed?
My favourite memory as a kid is of barbecues with my family in our garden. I never had burgers! Instead, we prepared a baguette filled with pork-loin fillet and *Iberico* ham or *pata negra*. It was delicious!

And in terms of a food product did you have a 'guilty pleasure'?
A traditional Spanish sweet bread called *Roscon de Reyes* which is absolutely
my guilty pleasure. However, it's only eaten on 6 January when we celebrate
what we call 'Wise Men Day'. So I have to wait to have it once a year!

What is your favourite meal after training and why do you like it?
I have many meals that I love from the training ground such as the famous
AXA LFC lasagne which I consider a 'comfort' dish. But what I really appreciate
are the 'live' cooking stations where the food is freshly-made.

And what is your favourite meal at home and why do you like it?
I am very lucky because my wife cooks just like a professional chef and she
also has knowledge of nutrition. She cooks *paella* in a healthy, fabulous way.

For breakfast: baked eggs, omelette, porridge, or protein pot?
I am an omelette lover.

And for dessert...?
My favourite is a coconut mousse with fresh passion fruit.

What is your favourite fruit and vegetable?
I love all kinds of fruits because my parents had a greengrocers in Seville.
My favourites are watermelon and strawberries which are often grown in
southern Spain. I am not the biggest fan of vegetables but I eat them!

"THERE ARE MANY MEALS WHICH I LOVE FROM THE TRAINING GROUND BUT WHAT I REALLY APPRECIATE ARE THE 'LIVE' COOKING STATIONS WHERE THE FOOD IS FRESHLY MADE"

FOODIE GUIDE TO SPAIN

Way to go?
In Europe's southwest corner, Spain shares its peninsula with Portugal. It's also neighboured by France to the north and has a Mediterranean and Atlantic coastline.

Say what?
Castilian Spanish is spoken by 72 per cent of the population. Galician and Basque are spoken in the north, while Adrian's native Andalucia has its own accent.

What's cooking?
Vegetables, fruits and cereals account for three-quarters of Spain's agricultural production, while olive oil, jamon (ham), chorizo (sausage) and wine are also big exports.

As a cook, how would you rate yourself between 1 and 5 (with 5 the highest score)?
Could I say zero? [modestly] I have to confess that I do not cook much. Having my wife at home and the chefs at Kirkby, I never wanted to enter into that restricted area!

If you could choose one team-mate to be your 'cooking buddy' who would it be?
Definitely Takumi Minamino. I love Japanese food and he won a cooking contest we did between team-mates. But hey, I had the second place and Fabinho had the third.

At LFC what's the best thing you have learned about good food and the right nutrition?
The benefits of vegan cuisine. Protein is a big source for athletes for gaining muscle and repairing tissue after training sessions and games. At LFC I have learned to prioritise vegetable protein instead of meat because it is healthier and more sustainable.

During the day, how do you try to stay hydrated?
I try to drink lot of water and also like to add electrolytes in a glass with plenty of water. [Electrolytes are salts and minerals in the body that maintain fluid-balance.]

Have you ever tried 'Scouse' and what did you think?
Yes and I loved it! Scouse reminds me of a traditional Spanish dish called *patatas guisadas con carne*.

What is the best smell in a kitchen or canteen?
I love that smell of when something delicious is cooking in the oven such a fresh, homemade bread.

Fab's Pancakes

FABINHO

YOU CAN'T BEAT THE SMELL OF PANCAKES!

—

BUT IT'S BRAZILIAN SPECIALITIES ALL THE WAY FOR DEFENSIVE MIDFIELD MAESTRO, FABINHO

Fab, what is the most popular dish in your home country?
In Brazil one of the most popular would be *feijoada*. It is black beans with some pork meat and is generally served with rice and some vegetables as well.

Sometimes in Brazil it's served with something called *farofa* which is a side dish [a type of toasted cornflour mix] with slices of orange. It's a meal I really enjoy.

When you were growing up as a kid, was there a favourite meal that the family all enjoyed?
On Sundays we would often have a lasagne which I always enjoyed.

And in terms of a food product did you have a 'guilty pleasure'?
I guess I liked the fast-food restaurants and having burgers and things like that!

What is your favourite meal after training at Kirkby and why do you like it?
We are very lucky in that we have a wide variety of food which is freshly-prepared for us by the chefs. I tend to have quite a lot of rice but there is always a good choice available.

And what is your favourite meal at home and why do you like it?
Generally at home we usually eat quite a lot of rice too, and we enjoy it with something like beef or chilli.

For breakfast: baked eggs, omelette, porridge, or protein pot?
I usually have eggs and a glass of water.

What is your favourite fruit and veg?
For fruit I'll say mango, and for veggies I don't know if I have a favourite... probably broccoli.

As a cook, how would you rate yourself between 1 and 5 (with 5 the highest score)?
Only a 'one', I'm afraid, as I'm not too good – but my wife is a very good cook which is lucky for me!

If you could choose one team-mate to be your 'cooking buddy' who would it be and why?
Adrian. I think he's a good chef and I enjoy Spanish food so I think he'd be a good choice.

Since you have been with LFC, what is the most important thing you have learned about good food and the right nutrition?
I have learned a few things and certainly a lot since the start of my career. Back then I didn't pay as much attention to what I ate or didn't think 100 per cent about healthy food, but now I try to eat much more healthily.

Here at Liverpool we always eat a lot of healthy food and we have a lot of variety in the kitchen too. We appreciate how important a good diet is to keeping us fit and healthy.

The support we had from the club during lockdown was very important because obviously we had to stay at home. It was very important that we still ate the correct things because we weren't quite sure when we were going to be able to start training and playing again and the club helped us out with deliveries to make sure that we were eating well, because if you are not training normally or eating the right foods, this could be a problem.

As I say, during that time we weren't sure when we were going to come back, so the help from the club and Mona especially was really important.

During the day, how do you try to stay hydrated?
I try to drink water. I know Brazil is known for producing coffee and I will occasionally have a cup of coffee or some tea, but it is not something I have every day.

In your opinion, what is the best smell in a kitchen or canteen?
I love the smell of pancakes. When I know we are having them, I always enjoy that smell.

What has been the funniest situation in the canteen?
During lockdown, Adrian, Taki, and me had some cooking lessons on video. As I say I am not very good in the kitchen, so it was a new experience! We made some Asian food. To be honest, it wasn't bad!

FOODIE GUIDE TO BRAZIL

Way to go?
Brazil is the largest country in South America and the fifth largest in the world. It forms an enormous triangle on the continent with a 4,500-mile coastline along the Atlantic Ocean, and it has borders with every South American country except Chile and Ecuador. It's very famous for its love of football and the legendary Maracana stadium in Rio de Janeiro.

Say what?
Portuguese is the main language for the vast majority of Brazilians, around 98 per cent of the population. The language has undergone many changes since it was first introduced to Brazil in the 16th century. A small percentage of Brazilians speak German and indigenous languages.

What's cooking?
Rice and beans is extremely popular – a tradition Brazil shares with several Caribbean nations. The nation is also known for its barbecued meat and salgadinhos – small savoury snacks, literally 'salties', similar to Spanish tapas and popular at family get-togethers.

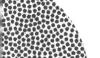

NABY KEITA

MANGOS
STRAIGHT OFF
THE TREE

—

MIDFIELDER NABY KEITA DESCRIBES THE FABULOUS FOOD BACK HOME IN GUINEA

Naby, when you were a child what was your favourite meal?
We had a dish called kansiye. It has a hot sauce and a lot of spices to it – you could burn your mouth on it.

And was there anything which was kept as a treat for being good?
Chocolate or *Nutella*!

What is your favourite dish at the training ground?
Pasta bolognese. Always after training, pasta bolognese! My brother really likes that too. Always after training when I go home, my brother asks what are we going to have to eat, and the answer is always pasta bolognese!

Do you cook at home yourself sometimes?
Yes, African food all the time for my younger brother. I cook the same things as my mother, but for him. Meat and tomato, cooked for a long time. Then potatoes and rice, mixed vegetables and the sauce on top.
 I have pasta bolognese although my brother also likes to have that kind of dish from time to time.

What would be a favourite fruit or vegetable from your part of Africa?
Mango. We have great mangos there – the smaller kind. We have mango straight off the tree. Everyone loves this kind of fruit over there.

 We have avocados as well and maracuya [passion fruit], the yellow ones. There are a lot of bananas grown in Guinea too, but mango is the most popular fruit in Africa.

If you could choose one team-mate to be your 'cooking buddy' who would it be?
Robbo and Virgil – both at the same time. We once made recipes together with Mona at Melwood!

What do you like to drink most?
Water, lots of water, although then sometimes in the night I have difficulty sleeping through! But water is very healthy.

What was the funniest moment you have experienced in the kitchen?
One time I was meant to be cooking fish in a frying pan and I forgot to add in

"ONE TIME I WAS MEANT TO BE COOKING FISH IN A FRYING PAN AND I FORGOT TO ADD THE COOKING OIL!"

FOODIE GUIDE TO GUINEA

the cooking oil. I got distracted and then I saw that I was burning the whole thing.

I went to add the oil and was afraid as it all went up like this *[flames]*... Suddenly it was all ablaze, so now I am always a bit anxious and keep a good distance when cooking!

Way to go?
Guinea is in western Africa on the Atlantic coast. Three of the region's major rivers – the Gambia, Niger and Senegal – rise in Guinea, which is abundant in natural resources including diamonds, gold and other metals.

Say what?
The official language is French, which was inherited from colonial rule. Several indigenous languages have been given national status : Fula or Pular, Malinke or Maninka, Susu, Kissi, Kpelle and Loma.

What's cooking?
Poulet yassa is a chicken dish prepared with onions, lemon or mustard. Other favourites include fou fou, a savoury pastry with okra sauce, cooked mango and fried sweet potatoes. Among the crops grown are cassava, sweet potatoes, bananas, coconuts, coffee and cacao.

JÜRGEN KLOPP

BOOM!

A QUICK-FIRE QUESTIONNAIRE WITH MANAGER JÜRGEN KLOPP

Popular dish back in Germany: Käsespätzle, a cheese-and-pasta dish.

Favourite family meal when you were growing up: See above!

Favourite meal after training at Kirkby: Chicken legs.

Favourite meal at home: [My wife] Ulla's chili.

Breakfast choice: Baked eggs.

Dessert choice: Cheesecake.

Favourite fruit and veg: Apples and broccoli.

As a cook how would you rate yourself between 1 and 5? Zero!

Staying hydrated: Water and tea.

Ever tried 'Scouse'? Yes, I like it.

Best smell in a kitchen: Barbecue.

JOEL'S PIZZA
THE ACTION

Centre-back Joel Matip likes to keep it simple as far as a 'guilty pleasure' goes. The Bochum-born defender explains that he is partial to a pizza. "I'd go for something classic like a margherita [cheese and tomato]. The German people always love sausage, so I like some types of sausage dishes too. Those are the two foods I really like. I don't have pizza too often but a good pizza is always nice."

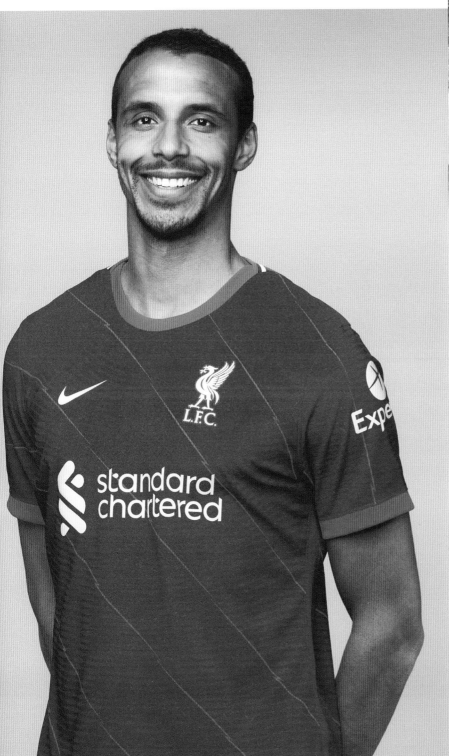

FOODIE GUIDE TO GERMANY

Way to go?
Germany is in central Europe and has borders with several other nations like France, the Netherlands, Denmark, Poland, the Czech Republic and Austria. Its big cities include Berlin, Munich and Hamburg, and three of its biggest rivers are the Rhine, Oder and Danube.

Say what?
Over 95 per cent of the country's 83 million people speak German as their first language. Minority languages include Sorbian (in the east) and North Frisian (far north).

What's cooking?
Konigsberger klopse is a dish of meatballs in a creamy sauce with capers. Other favourites include bratwurst sausage, maultaschen (pasta with meat-filling similar to Italian ravioli) and schnitzel (thin slices of fried meat).

TAKUMI MINAMINO

IT'S SUSHI AND MISO EVERY TIME!

MIDFIELDER TAKUMI MINAMINO EXPLAINS WHAT'S
SO SPECIAL ABOUT JAPANESE CUISINE

Taki, what is the most famous food from your country?
Sushi is the best-known food. In Germany [Taki played for RB Salzburg in neighbouring Austria] there is some good variety and high quality, probably at the same level that you get in Japan. But the really typical sushi dishes are the kind of dishes you can only get in Japan – and very expensive!

Which is your favourite kind of sushi?
My favourite is prawns. We Japanese normally only eat sushi prawns as a nigiri [literally 'two fingers'] dish. We say that only nigiri sushi is real sushi!

And as a child what was your favourite thing to eat?
Steak or meat. Beef was always my favourite, as prepared by my mother, maybe with mashed potatoes and carrots. Not really rice.

What is your occasional treat?
Big Mac hamburgers! Maybe Kentucky Fried Chicken at times. KFC!

And what is your favourite kind of food for breakfast?
I like toast just with butter or maybe sometimes with jam on. There are some really good jams available in Austria.

What would constitute a typical Japanese breakfast?
Rice with a traditional *miso* soup and some fish – any kind, with rice in the soup. The soup is a drink. There are various kinds, many varieties, but the miso my mother would make comprised of onions, potatoes and tofu – those three ingredients.

So then do you have a high energy-level all day long after such a breakfast?
Yes!

What is your favourite fruit and vegetables to eat?
I like strawberries and pineapple. Vegetable-wise I'd say potatoes as they are so versatile. Also asparagus, and spinach is another favourite of mine. You see it quite a lot in Japanese cuisine.

How do you rate yourself as a cook?
Well, okay but not really that good. I can't really cook anything but if I had to, I guess I could come up with something.

Who would you pick out from among your team-mates to cook with?
Only from the players? Adrian. We did cook together once, it was for a 'Liverpool Challenge' Foundation event, I think. Adri, me and Fab, so he made cakes. I was interested in Spanish cooking – paella and so on.

What is your favourite drink?
Sparkling water. I sometimes have it with a little bit of lemon and always drank it when I was playing in Austria. I also enjoy sparkling apple-juice [one-third apple juice and two-thirds sparkling water, a famously refreshing drink in sport].

Have you ever tried Scouse?
Yes, I've tried it and enjoyed it – very tasty.

What is your favourite smell in the kitchen?
Roasting meat, that's the one for me. It really takes me back to my childhood.

Have you ever had a really funny experience in the kitchen?
I can think of one that was more frightening than funny. When I was a youngster, my mother was preparing the evening meal, and I have an older brother who really wanted to help out. So he set about peeling the potatoes and managed to cut himself – quite a big cut. I'd wanted to help out and get involved, too, but when I saw that cut I thought: better not – just let her get on with it!

FOODIE GUIDE TO JAPAN

—

Way to go?
Japan is an island off the east coast of the Asian landmass. It consists of a great string of islands that stretches for approximately 1,500 miles through the western North Pacific Ocean.

Say what?
Japanese is divided into several dialects with the Tokyo variety considered standard. Other similar languages are spoken in Okinawa and parts of Kagoshima in the Ryukyu Islands.

What's cooking?
Sushi is a dish of short-grain rice that is lightly 'vinegared' and then served with a selection of raw or cooked fish and vegetables. It's usually prepared before diners and very elegantly presented in a sliced wrap of seaweed, sometimes with a very hot type of horseradish called wasabi. Other dishes include sashimi (finely-sliced raw fish and seafood), tempura (deep-fried seafood, meat and veg), soba (buckwheat noodles) and yakitori (grilled chicken skewers).

The JOY of SCOUSE

IT'S NOT JUST AN ACCENT AND A REGIONAL IDENTITY – IT'S A MUCH-LOVED TRADITIONAL RECIPE WITH A SEAFARING STORY BORN IN THE HEART OF LIVERPOOL

Stews come in all styles, shapes and sizes around the world – and not just for the winter months – and they are particularly popular in South America and South East Asia as well as European countries like Spain, Portugal and Italy.

Stews are often described as hearty and rustic – in other words, they fill you up, they are simple and inexpensive, and they're 'good for you'. Traditionally stew was known as 'peasant food' with many of the classic recipes come from working-class or poorer communities, and every region and family seemed to have its own version. Some have not only stood the test of time but become super fashionable.

The word 'stew' in English means to cook slowly, usually but not always in a thick, chunky soup. As a rule it's quite a rich dish and there is nothing wrong with that. Flavour-wise, though, it pays to use the right cuts of meat.

For a chicken stew, for example, it's best not to use the breast because its structure is not made to be cooked for a long time. Instead go for boneless chicken thighs or drumsticks.

Similarly for a beef stew, avoid fillet or sirloin. Try cheaper cuts like shin, shoulder (also known as chuck) or oxtail which cook better for longer –

turning soft and tender – and are full of flavour. These parts of the meat will also combine beautifully with vegetables like onions, potatoes and carrots to give the stew the best taste and colour.

Of course the Liverpool version is known as Scouse and its origins lie in the city's history as one of the greatest ports in the world. The word is a shortened version of 'lobscouse' which is thought to be the name of a dish imported by Scandinavian seaman centuries ago. Today it's similar to both Irish Stew and Lancashire Hotpot, but it's very much a Liverpudlian thing.

You can bet that the likes of Trent Alexander-Arnold and before him Steven Gerrard, Jamie Carragher and Robbie Fowler have all had a few bowls of Scouse in their time. Indeed a few years ago another local lad, former striking ace John Aldridge, celebrated the annual Global Scouse Day by sampling the chef's own recipe at Anfield's Boot Room Sports Café.

Among the ingredients were chuck steak, diced onion, swede, carrots and peeled and diced potatoes, plus beef stock, olive oil, a sprig of thyme and bay leaves – garnished with pickled beetroot and pickled cabbage (both high in vitamin C) and chunky white bread and butter. The cooking took around two hours and Aldo declared it as good if not better than his mum's own recipe!

More recently the LFC matchday programme for that unforgettable Champions League semi-final second leg against Barcelona at Anfield in May 2019 featured a recipe for Catalan Scouse, courtesy of local restaurant Lunya.

It included minced lamb, spicy *chorizo* and *morcilla* (Spanish sausages) along with potatoes, carrots, onion, garlic, paprika (a spice made from ground peppers), meat or vegetable stock and a side dish of pickled artichokes.

Lunya owner Peter Kinsella revealed it was "one of our best-selling dishes, extravagant and flavoursome. It could sit in either city [Liverpool or Barcelona] and be recognised, except that in Spain they would call it *fabada*."

In Liverpool there is also a delicious vegan version known historically as 'Blind Scouse' – the same stew but without meat and made by adding leeks, pearl barley and butter beans, for instance, to the other vegetables.

Either way, Scouse is great served straightaway or chilled in the fridge overnight and reheated the next day – and it can feed families at little expense.

JOE GOMEZ

I'VE LEARNED SO MUCH FROM MONA

—

CENTRE-BACK JOE GOMEZ ON STRAWBERRIES, SWEET POTATO AND HIS MUM'S SPAGHETTI

Joe, when you were growing up was there a favourite dish that the family all enjoyed?
I think because of the African influence of my dad [who is Gambian], he was always trying out different sauces and so there were a lot of things we used to enjoy as a family.

My dad would probably have a rice-and-chicken dish with various sauces as his go-to which were always good, and my mum made a fabulous spaghetti bolognese too.

In terms of a food product did you have a 'guilty pleasure'?
When I was younger, the area of London where I was from used to have a Nando's with a dessert place nearby. It used to be a bit of a routine after training or a match to go to Nando's first then go across to have a dessert – usually ice-cream and waffles.

What's your favourite meal after training and why do you like it?
After training it's usually about fuelling the body. I enjoy chicken and sweet potato and that's probably my favourite, although I'm always buzzing if the chefs have prepared chicken legs or chicken wings too.

And what's your favourite meal at home?
To be honest, I'm still quite basic at the moment so If I'm making something I usually do a stir-fry or spaghetti bolognese. My missus is very good, though, and she makes a great stir-fry.

For breakfast: baked eggs, omelette, porridge, or protein pot?
My staple breakfast is strawberries and granola with yoghurt and maybe some eggs on the side.

What is your favourite fruit?
Definitely strawberries!

As a cook, how would you rate yourself between 1 and 5 (with 5 the highest score)?
I'd say a steady three!

If you could choose one team-mate to be your 'cooking buddy' who would it be?
Probably Virg because I don't think he'd be any good and I could take the mickey out of him! There'd be plenty of banter if we paired up in the kitchen.

Since you have been with LFC, what is the most important thing you have learned about good food and the right nutrition?
Everything. It's changed my whole perspective and outlook. I've learned so much from Mona about carbs, proteins, fats, minerals and what the right thing is to eat. My understanding has completely evolved.
  To be honest, when I joined the club I had just turned 18 and didn't have a clue about food. Now I have a far better understanding but I know there is so much more to learn. It's helped make a huge difference to football and

professional sport in general as we understand better the importance of how food can aid recovery between matches and help keep us fit and sharp. I think the days of players having beers in the week have long gone!

Mona's been unbelievable. During the first national lockdown she was incredible with providing food-parcels and so on for us all and, as I say, she's helped change my outlook entirely.

There is so much data available now and we understand that fuelling the right way can aid recovery and hopefully help us have longer careers.

During the day, how do you try to stay hydrated?
Mainly water. I do enjoy a coffee and maybe have a couple a day, but it's mainly water for hydration and I sometimes add electrolytes for a bit of flavour.

Have you ever tried 'Scouse' and what did you think?
I have actually as they'll sometimes put it on for us in the canteen. I have to say I'm a fan!

What is the best smell in a kitchen or canteen?
Probably pancakes when I walk into the canteen for breakfast. There are always some great smells when I go in at breakfast-time.

What have you made of the canteen facilities at the new training ground?
They are fantastic as is every aspect of it, to be honest. It's been refreshing to come to a new environment with such incredible facilities and it makes going in an even bigger pleasure.

FOOD AND FAVOURITE DISHES
FROM AROUND BRITAIN

The UK produces nearly 14 million tonnes of dairy milk each year.

Strawberries remain Britain's most popular soft fruit, but in second place more blueberries (once only imported from overseas) are now grown than raspberries. Other favourites include plums, cranberries, blackberries and currants.

With its fields of bright yellow, British rapeseed oil is becoming more and more popular in cooking. It has similar benefits to olive oil but arguably has more flavour.

Broad beans are grown all over the UK. They're best enjoyed fresh in late spring and early summer and they're loaded with nutrients.

NORTH WEST

England's North West is famous for Lancashire Hotpot (a slow-cooked meat stew like Scouse), black pudding (usually as part of a Full English Breakfast), Cheshire cheese, and sweet and sticky Eccles cakes.

EAST MIDLANDS

Some of the finest apples in the world are grown in British orchards. The East Midlands is famous for its Bramley variety (great for cooking with), along with Melton Mowbray pork pie and Red Leicester cheese.

GLOUCESTERSHIRE

How do you like your eggs? They range from the delicate blue shells of the Cotswold Legbar to the dark-coloured Burford Brown, thought to have been introduced to Gloucestershire from Patagonia a century ago.

CHANNEL ISLANDS

Potatoes, carrots, turnips and onions are Britain's most-grown vegetables. Among potatoes alone, there are hundreds of different varieties. Jersey Royals, grown only on the Channel island of the same name, are probably the most famous of all. Among the many others: King Edwards, Maris Piper, Charlotte, Anya, Rooster and Vivaldi.

SCOTLAND

The national dish of Scotland is the hearty delicacy known as haggis – a large, round sausage filled with sheep offal, oats, fat, onion and spices. These days vegetarian haggis is also available.

WEST YORKSHIRE

Rhubarb, which is rich in antioxidants, thrives in a large triangular area of West Yorkshire and has an annual festival in its honour. Crispy on the outside and fluffy inside, Yorkshire pudding is a simple recipe made from eggs, flour, and milk. When you add sausages, it's called Toad in the Hole. Also from Yorkshire: Wensleydale cheese, as loved by Wallace and Gromit!

BRADFORD

Bradford is a serial winner of Britain's curry capital award, but people in every city love their biryani, rogan josh, bhuna, madras and tikka masala!

EAST ANGLIA

East Anglia is the home of the distinctive, blue-veined Stilton cheese. It also boasts lots of arable land for growing cereal crops like wheat, oats and barley. Every day an estimated 11 million loaves of bread are made in the UK using mostly British wheat, while 11,000 loaves can be made from a single hectare of wheat – about the size of the pitch at Anfield.

WALES

Wales has several national dishes including Welsh rarebit (cheese on toast), bara brith (fruit cake) and Conwy mussels.

CORNWALL

Cornish pasties come from (obviously) Cornwall and consist of minced beef and vegetables in a shortcrust, savoury pastry. The southwest region is also home to Cheddar cheese and livestock farming (cattle, pigs, poultry).

ISLE OF WIGHT

Garlic is big business in the Isle of Wight, which even has its own festival for this close relative of the onion with proven health benefits.

STIR-FRY FOR MILLY

A QUICK-FIRE QUESTIONNAIRE WITH
VICE-CAPTAIN JAMES MILNER

—

Favourite family meal when you were growing up: Turkey parcels – very tasty!

'Guilty pleasure': Apple crumble.

Favourite meal after training at Kirkby: Stir-fry.

Favourite meal at home: Steak.

Breakfast choice: I make porridge at home because it's easy.

Dessert choice: Crumble and custard.

Favourite fruit and veg: Berries, apples and bananas, and broccoli.

As a cook how would you rate yourself between 1 and 5? One – but my wife Amy's a five!

One team-mate as your 'cooking buddy': Robbo because I've never tried haggis.

Most important thing about the right nutrition: You can enjoy a variety of food and still be healthy.

Staying hydrated: I drink water regularly.

Ever tried 'Scouse'? Yes, it was decent.

Best smell in a kitchen: Onions cooking – I prefer the smell to the taste!

JORDAN HENDERSON

SKIPPER'S NOTES

—

AFTER LIFTING THE PREMIER LEAGUE TROPHY IN THE 2019/20 SEASON, HENDO WROTE THIS IN HIS MATCHDAY PROGRAMME COLUMN...

"Behind the team there are so many different individuals and groups who make a side successful. At Liverpool every single player in our dressing-room recognises how fortunate we are to have the best in the world looking out for us and after us.

"Aside from the fans, the other support network we have is the staff who work for this club, specifically the guys at the training ground, but also those we don't get to see as often. A club as big as Liverpool can only operate successfully if every employee performs to their highest level. That's what we have here, off the pitch as much as on the pitch.

"Each day we are looked after by world-class professionals who create a culture and environment where players can thrive. Whether it's the coaches, the medical team, fitness staff, the nutrition experts and chefs, the ground staff, the administration people or security...they dedicate their careers to make our team the best it can be.

"It is no exaggeration to say that without these people the team would not be what it is. Without them the training ground would feel different and not give us the same energy. I hope everyone there knows how important they are to us and realise this title is as much for them as anyone."

CAPTAIN'S TABLE

JORDAN HENDERSON ON SUNDAY ROASTS AND THE SMELL OF FRESH BREAD

—

Favourite family meal when you were growing up: Sunday roast.
'Guilty pleasure': Jellies.
Favourite meal after training at Kirkby: Chicken pesto pasta.
Favourite meal at home: Chicken or beef stir-fry.
Breakfast choice: Omelette or porridge.
Dessert choice: Cheesecake.
Favourite fruit and veg: Strawberry and sweet potato.
As a cook how would you rate yourself between 1 and 5? Two.
One team-mate as your 'cooking buddy': Robbo because it would be fun!
Most important thing about the right nutrition: Everything in moderation, and I've also become more aware of what foods I have on certain days.
Staying hydrated: Try to have two litres of water throughout the day.
Ever tried 'Scouse'? Only at Melwood but yes, it was nice.
Best smell in a kitchen: Fresh bread.
Funniest foodie moment: The chefs at our training-ground arguing over different types of sauce!

Mona on...
LFC'S LEAGUE of NATIONS

NO TWO PLAYERS ARE THE SAME BUT THE CLUB'S NUTRITIONAL 'CURRICULUM' ENABLES SENIOR STARS AND YOUNG PROSPECTS TO LEARN MORE ABOUT FOOD

"When you have players from lots of different countries, as we do at LFC, it's very interesting not just from a nutritional point-of-view but culturally too.

"What kind of foods have they grown up eating? What do they like? What are they accustomed to eating – not just from home but from playing in other countries as well?

"Before we really start to look at a player's diet, we need to have a lot of information, a kind of food 'history' from the individual in question: his preferences and interests and the things he trusts. That's where we begin.

"Then, based on conversations, we do an analysis of his food 'traditions'. We look at what might be genetic-based, what is 'soul'-based – food that he associates with home and family and memories, for example – and also where any issues or problems might sit.

"Then we have the possibility to take samples like saliva, blood, urine and stools, and make things like subcutaneous fat [stored just under the skin] measurements.

"Eventually we will have what we call the complete 'portfolio' plus the player's own summary, and we can look at whether we need an adjustment of nutrition. Is it a medical and nutritional interaction? Is there a supplement-based issue, any deficiencies or inflammations in the body? So that's actually how we build up a nutritional profile.

"A former player of mine, from back in Germany, went to play in the Middle East and called me and left a message. He said the football wasn't going so well but the lifestyle was brilliant and could I send him a nutrition plan?! But it's impossible to do from such a distance and it would be unprofessional, too, without knowing his specific situation.

"Seasonal, locally-sourced food is fabulous and so important to what we do, but at the same time players don't have to adapt to an absolutely new diet just because they are in a different country. We are all so globally-connected these days that we can buy any type of food product from almost everywhere in the world, so the players don't really feel a huge difference in that respect.

"The differences are more emotional, really – the 'soul food' that I mentioned. What you grew up with and your memories. Maybe when you had a cold and your mum cooked something special at home. Specific smells or tastes that remind you – 'Just like Mama used to make!'

"Every player tends to have a routine that he trusts or likes to stick to. He might even be a little suspicious of something new. If something works for you and you have the feeling that you've prepared yourself in the right way, there's nothing wrong in that.

"When it comes to food-intake, some players are simply 'mono-eaters'! They are happy with having pasta every day and knowing its benefits. It's still one of the very classic things that players love to eat, especially on matchdays. What we might try to do is educate them to 'create the plate' a bit differently, using other carbohydrate sources.

"Likewise some players really love their food and like to try new things. Dejan

Lovren was really into his cooking when he was here. Alisson Becker is a big fan of barbecues which is a friends-and-family thing: everyone getting together to enjoy the meal, have fun, listen to music – maybe Ali on his guitar! So food performs a social role. It's part of the entertainment. It makes people happy, especially when you're in a group.

"Lots of nationalities are like this. The Italians are famous for having big family dinners. The Spanish share *tapas*. The French have things like *fondues* – a melted cheese dish for everyone. But I guess it's all down to your personality and whether you like to have a lot of people around.

"It's nice to see the younger players taking an interest, too. Nat Phillips, for example, is very handy in the kitchen. When he was on loan in Germany he discovered and tried a vegan diet on his own.

"I think the next generation of players are becoming more aware about nutrition in this country. We have a curriculum at LFC, something we started compiling about five years ago now, and there's a progression it for young players to learn and understand more about food as they become older, along with practical workshops with chefs for different age-groups.

"For the older groups, especially if they are about to move out from their 'house parents' or normal parents and get their own place, there are things like how to prepare your breakfast at home, or how to create a pre-match snack.

"Obviously we speak to coaches and people in charge to manage these things around their diaries because they have school and home and training and it needs to fit in correctly. So pre-season and half-terms, when they have a bit more time, are really useful. And as well as learning, they are creating good habits and life-skills: how to behave and how to help each other too."

THE LANGUAGE

ENGLISH	FRENCH	GERMAN	ITALIAN	DUTCH
Enjoy your meal!	Bon appetit!	Guten appetit!	Buon appetito!	Eet smakelijk!
It's delicious	C'est délicieux	Es schmeckt sehr lecker	È delizioso	Het is lekker
Food	Nourriture	Lebensmittel	Cibo	Voedsel
Breakfast	Petit-déjeuner	Frühstück	Prima colazione	Ontbijt
Lunch	Déjeuner	Mittagessen	Pranzo	Lunch
Dinner	Dîner	Abendessen	Cena	Avondeten
Dessert	Dessert	Nachtisch	Dolce	Toetje
Snack	Collation	Zwischenmahlzeit	Spuntino	Tussendoortje
Kitchen	Cuisine	Küche	Cucina	Keuken
Oven	Four	Backofen	Forno	Oven
Recipe	Recette	Rezept	Ricetta	Recept
Cook	Cuisiner	Ein gericht kochen	Cucinare	Koken
Bake	Cuire	Backen	Infornare	Bakken
Boil	Bouillir	Etwas kochen	Bollire	Koken
Fry	Faire frire	Braten	Friggere	Braden
Grill	Griller	Grillen	Griglia	Grillen
Meat	Viande	Fleisch	Carne	Vlees
Fish	Poisson	Fisch	Pesce	Vis
Fruit	Fruit	Früchte	Frutta	Fruit
Vegetable	Légume	Gemüse	Verdura	Groente
Bread	Pain	Brot	Pane	Brood
Water	Eau	Wasser	Acqua	Water
Sugar	Sucre	Zucker	Zucchero	Suiker
Salt	Sel	Salz	Sale	Zout

OF LOVE!

WORDS FOR FOOD FROM AROUND THE WORLD

SPANISH	PORTUGUESE	GREEK	ARABIC	JAPANESE
Buen provecho!	Bom apetite!	Καλή όρεξη!	بالعافية!	お召し上がりください
Está delicioso	É deliciosa	Είναι νόστιμα	إنه لذيذ	おいしいです
Comida	Comida	Φαγητό	طعام	食物
Desayuno	Café da manhã	Πρωινό	وجبة الإفطار	朝ごはん
Almuerzo	Almoço	Μεσημεριανό	الغداء	昼ごはん
Cena	Jantar	Βραδινό	وجبة العشاء	晩ごはん
Postre	Sobremesa	Επιδόρπιο	الحلوى	デザート
Merienda	Lanche	Πρόχειρο φαγητό	وجبة خفيفة	軽食
Cocina	Cozinha	Κουζίνα	مطبخ	台所
Horno	Forno	Φούρνος	فرن	オーブン
Receta	Receita	Συνταγή	وصفة	レシピ
Cocinar	Cozinhar	Μάγειρας	يطبخ	料理する
Hornear	Assar	Ψήνω	خبز	オーブンで焼く
Hervir	Ferver	Βρασμός	غلى	ゆでる
Freir	Fritar	Μαρίδα	يقلى	揚げる
Asar a la parilla	Grelhar	ψηνω στα καρβουνα	شوي	網で焼く
Carne	Carne	Κρέας	لحم	肉
Pescado	Peixe	Ψάρι	سمك	魚
Fruta	Fruta	Καρπός	فاكهة	果物
Verdura	Vegetal	Λαχανικό	الخضروات	野菜
Pan	Pão	Ψωμί	خبز	パン
Agua	Água	Νερό	ماء	水
Azúcar	Açúcar	Ζάχαρη	السكر	砂糖
Sal	Sal	Αλας	ملح	塩

PLENTY AT STEAK

HOW THE REDS BEEFED UP TO BECOME CHAMPIONS

In today's 'global village' we can get foodstuffs from pretty much every corner of the wold with ease, but that wasn't the case when Liverpool FC won their fifth top-flight title in 1946/47.

Indeed one of the reasons why the Reds were crowned champions, according to football historians, was the fact that they'd sailed off from food-rationed Britain to the USA for their pre-season tour and boosted their diets.

It's hard to imagine now but during the Second World War and for years afterwards, food was scarce in many countries including the UK. Among the products in short supply were beef, bacon, ham, butter, sugar, tea, bread, cheese and canned goods.

People could only purchase them with coupons from what were called 'ration books'. A cartoon in the *Liverpool Echo* newspaper even joked that player rationing would be next!

Of course the war was the biggest factor in the food shortages, but heavy rain over the summer of 1946 ruined much of Britain's wheat crop, then a long hard winter destroyed a huge amount of potatoes. Indeed food rationing only ended in 1954.

With this in mind, and having previously

Legendary Reds boss Bill Shankly watches new signing Alun Evans tuck into chicken and eggs!

visited North America on catering business, Liverpool FC chairman Bill McConnell had a brilliant idea in 1946: feed big juicy steaks and hamburgers and lots of eggs to the players on a tour of the United States to prepare them for the resumption of league football after the war.

The nutritional science may not have been advanced as it is these days, but it was clear that consuming protein from sources like meat was crucial for muscle growth and recovery.

Under manager George Kay, the Reds duly won all of their ten games on tour and the *New York Times* reported that the team had averaged "a gain in weight of seven pounds a man."

Back home Liverpool would pip Manchester United to the 1946/47 First Division title by a point, having won seven of their last eight fixtures and also reached the semi-finals of the FA Cup.

Over the next few decades, as more food became readily available, the diets of professional footballers were simple but generally effective. There is a famous picture from 1968 of Reds manager Bill Shankly standing over new signing Alun Evans while the young striker tucks into some roast chicken and hard-boiled eggs.

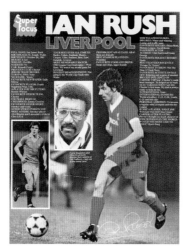

"AFTER EVERY AWAY GAME WE HAD EITHER CHICKEN AND CHIPS, FISH AND CHIPS, PIE AND CHIPS, OR SAUSAGE AND CHIPS!"

As recently as the 1980s there was still nowhere near the variety of foodstuffs (particularly from overseas) nor the nutritional research as there is today. In those days football magazines like *Shoot!* had regular Q&A interviews with players and the answer to the 'favourite food' questions always seemed to be 'steak and chips' – young scoring sensation Ian Rush being no exception in 1982.

Former Reds midfielder Jan Molby recently revealed to *The Athletic* website: "I'd always have a cheese and ham omelette three hours before kick-off and then a cup of tea with four sugars at half-time. Rushie's pre-match was a medium fillet steak with baked beans.

"After every away game there were four choices: chicken-and-chips, fish-and-chips, pie-and-chips or sausage-and-chips! Ronnie Moran [the first-team coach] would write it all down and we'd stop off at a takeaway to collect our order for the journey home. That was the refuelling back then."

Upon becoming Liverpool manager in 1991, former captain Graeme Souness was the first to introduce healthier meal options at the training ground – dishes such as boiled fish, boiled chicken, pasta and vegetables – and the coming of the Premier League ushered in a new era of food science at football clubs.

MAKING A
DIFFE

RED NEIGHBOURHOOD

RENCE

—

HOW LIVERPOOL FC'S FLYING FULL-BACKS HAVE HELPED TO FIGHT FOOD-POVERTY, AND HOW THE CLUB IS EMPOWERING YOUNG PEOPLE TO LEARN ABOUT NUTRITION

Good food and healthy eating play a huge part in Liverpool FC's community work, both at home and further afield. As the club's head of nutrition, Mona aims to use her food knowledge to help to make a positive difference to people's health and wellbeing, and in her fun and educational cookery classes she's been joined by the manager, current and former LFC players, plus coaches and club staff.

LOOKING OUT FOR EACH OTHER

———

Being part of Liverpool Football Club means being part of the greatest football family in the world. The message is simple: we look out for each other, and particularly those who are in need. To achieve this, there are two distinct sides to the club's community work: LFC Foundation and Red Neighbours.

LFC Foundation is the official charity of Liverpool Football Club. Building on the club's work in the community over the years, it was formed in 2010 to harness the power and passion our fans have to improve the lives of others.

Red Neighbours was launched a little later, at the start of 2017, as a new community programme to support local residents and schools in the Anfield area.

It focuses on four key areas of need, having spoken to people who live and work in the L4 postcode district, and one of them is food poverty and education. The other three are: support for the elderly community; encouraging a physically active community; and creating memorable experiences for young people.

That means organising events and experiences to support those four areas of need, and a small, dedicated team of LFC staff works together with local residents, 25 schools around the Anfield area, local community groups, key stakeholders, and other club staff who give their time and expertise voluntarily, to do just that.

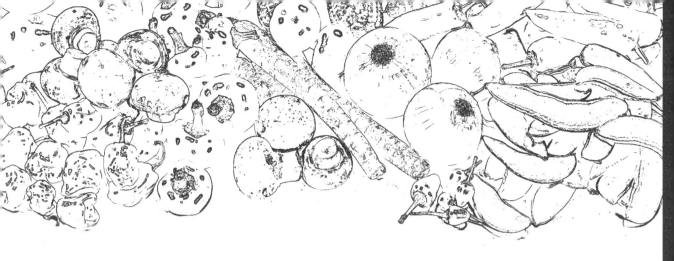

SAFE AND SOUND

——

If ever there was a time to look after ourselves and each other by eating the right food, this is it. A balanced diet can help us to stay fit, healthy and safe, with the right ingredients providing energy and the best nutrients to boost our immune systems.

The COVID-19 pandemic and its lockdowns meant that many people's eating habits changed. For some it was a chance to learn more about food and pass time by learning to cook and bake more, but for others it meant tough choices – making ends meet when it came to mealtimes.

Liverpool FC recognised these struggles and, as part of its Operation Christmas Magic campaign at the end of the unbelievably challenging year of 2020, the club and its charity LFC Foundation donated over £147,000 to support local families in food poverty.

Liverpool is ranked the fourth most deprived local authority area in the country (England has 353 local authorities) and its greatest concentration of deprivation is in the north of the city.

The funds were raised from LFC Legends Charity Match ticket refunds – the showcase game against Barcelona's team of ex-stars having been postponed because of the pandemic – plus sales of Levi's x LFC exclusive 'trucker jackets' and limited-edition tees, and donations from Anfield executive lounge and boardroom members.

All this paid for five new 'community pantries' across Liverpool helping to support 750 families every year, as well as support for seven existing Your Local pantries. An investment was also made into warehouse facilities at North Liverpool Foodbank, a delivery van for St Andrew's Community Network, and a new job role of foodbank and pantry coordinator.

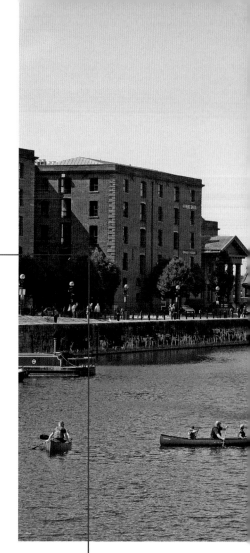

Previously, during the first UK lockdown, Liverpool FC wanted to be there as much as possible for those in need.

Whether that was supporting the NHS and frontline key workers or tackling food-poverty and social isolation, the club brought together its official charity, community programme and wider club staff in a coordinated response to the pandemic.

As well as donating personal protective equipment (PPE) and delivering 'goodie bags' and 'treat boxes', the club arranged telephone calls to older and more vulnerable members of the public – sometimes even chatting with Reds boss Jürgen Klopp and first-teamers Andy Robertson and Virgil van Dijk.

Also delivered each week were 1,000 fresh meals prepared by Liverpool FC's professional chefs as part of the club's 'Unity is Strength' COVID-19 community-response work.

They provided essential fuel to those who needed it most, including Merseyside Fire and Rescue Service firefighters and officers, North West Ambulance Service staff, and school hubs and community groups.

Red Neighbours senior manager Forbes Duff revealed at the time: "Since we started producing the meals we have seen a big uptake, so we've been working hard to increase our volumes.

"Helping those who are sacrificing so much to help others is important to us. If we can take the pressure off by providing a fresh meal, so they don't have to cook after a long shift, or for school hubs looking after vulnerable children and key workers' children, it's the least we can do to say thank you."

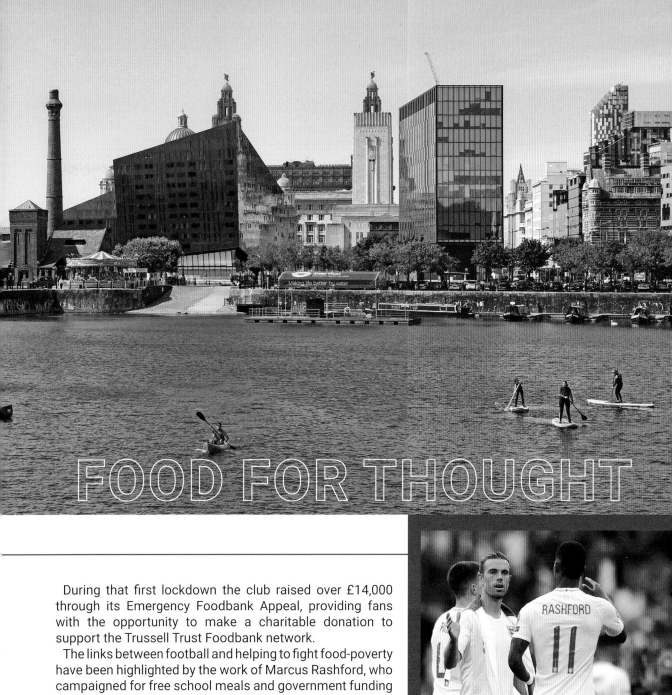

FOOD FOR THOUGHT

During that first lockdown the club raised over £14,000 through its Emergency Foodbank Appeal, providing fans with the opportunity to make a charitable donation to support the Trussell Trust Foodbank network.

The links between football and helping to fight food-poverty have been highlighted by the work of Marcus Rashford, who campaigned for free school meals and government funding to support the cost of food and household bills for poor families, and it eventually earned him an MBE.

Marcus may play for one of Liverpool's fiercest rivals in Manchester United, but everyone connected with LFC has nothing but the greatest admiration for his work. In the summer of 2020 the club tweeted: "Children in our region will benefit because of the actions of this remarkable role-model. From Liverpool With Love."

TRENT

A DIFFERENT KIND
OF ASSIST

—

The past few years have seen the club's Red Neighbours team up with Fans Supporting Foodbanks to help collect thousands of kilogrammes of food on matchdays for the North Liverpool Foodbank, in aid of local people in crisis.

Not only this, but Red Neighbours delivered free breakfast clubs for local families to attend during school half-term and summer holidays – more on that later.

Among the LFC stars keen to help out have been full-back pals Trent Alexander-Arnold and Andy Robertson. At the end of 2019, local lad Trent helped Red Neighbours launch its Christmas Foodbank Appeal, dropping by North Liverpool Foodbank to donate food, meet staff and volunteers and find out more about the centre's important work.

He declared: "I'm really proud that my club is supporting such an important cause. It was a pleasure to be able to visit the foodbank and meet with the hard-working staff and volunteers – their dedication makes such a difference to people who need their help."

Previously Robbo had done something similar, dropping off bags full

ROBBO

of donations at the St Andrew's Community Network near Anfield, to be distributed by the Foodbank.

The Scotland skipper, who has also supported food charities in his hometown of Glasgow, later told *The Big Issue* magazine: "It's incredible the amount of people that rely on foodbanks...and unfortunately that number is only going to get higher with what's going on in the world, just knowing people are losing jobs and things like that.

"So people that are fortunate enough to have a job and get paid well, I believe we can give that back because these people need us now probably more than ever."

Andy described Marcus Rashford as "a credit to football in the way he goes about his business... Forget any rivalry, it's nothing because we all have the same view as Marcus on this."

Robbo being Robbo, there's also been time for a bit of fun at his own expense. Two years ago, when he heard about a young Liverpool fan donating pocket-money to a foodbank, he sent him a signed shirt from team-mate and striker Bobby Firmino, joking: "No one wants the left-back's shirt!"

"A PRIVILEGE TO COME HERE"

———

Three years ago Nat Phillips was a young LFC Academy prospect with dreams of one day making his debut for the Reds first-team. And so he would, first in an FA Cup third-round tie against neighbours Everton at Anfield in January 2020, then in the Premier League in a home win over West Ham in October that same year, having returned from a loan-spell at German club VfB Stuttgart.

But in February 2018, as a regular for Liverpool's Under-23 side, he visited the North Liverpool Foodbank to lend a hand, along with team-mates Jordan Williams and Mich'el Parker.

The trio helped out with a variety of tasks, including helping to sort, weigh and pack food parcels, before learning about the vital work the foodbank did within the Anfield community.

Nat said: "Visiting has definitely been an eye-opener and it was a privilege for us to come here and give our support. It has been nice to see the volunteers and the selfless work they are doing to help other people."

A few months later fellow central defender and Estonian international Ragnar Klavan dropped by with a donation, as did Sadio Mane, while Liverpool and England midfielder Adam Lallana toured the facility and chatted to volunteers. Adam said: "It's extremely saddening to realise that foodbanks are part of everyday life for many local people but also very humbling to see the massive contribution made by fans – they have helped thousands of local people."

These visits by footballers, though, have helped to raise awareness of food-poverty and encourage donations. Before the pandemic meant that matches had to be played behind-closed-doors, collections were made three hours before kick-off (for Premier League games) at three locations around the ground – a foodbank van located on Anfield Road, the official LFC retail store and the Homebaked community bakery on nearby Oakfield Road.

Supporters could drop off essential non-perishable food items (and toiletries) including: UHT milk, long-life juice or cordial, coffee, pasta and curry sauce, tinned meat and vegetables, instant mash, rice-pudding and custard, jam, toiletries, cup-a-soup, noodles and washing tablets.

In turn these could be made into three-day emergency food-parcels for local residents in need.

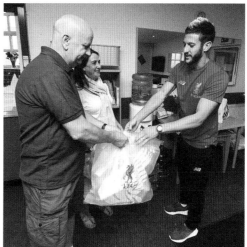

Matchday donations may have been suspended by the pandemic, but Fans Supporting Foodbanks was still very active with thousands of people on Merseyside relying on help to get them through the COVID-19 crisis.

Victoria Ponsonby, a coordinator at North Liverpool Foodbank, said: "We have always been extremely grateful for the support we get from Red Neighbours, not to mention the generous Liverpool fans."

She also explained to the *Liverpool Echo* newspaper: "During the first lockdown we definitely did deliver a lot of food.

"We were part of the council's plan in making sure that people who were isolated or shielded had access to food, so we did do that and we set up at Anfield Sports & Community Centre as a packing depot with fresh produce and fresh bread.

'We did that together with Liverpool FC, Everton FC and Food for Thought [a not-for-profit school meals company] and we made that happen really quickly."

During the second lockdown, added Victoria, "we were all prepared to set up another packing centre and do the same thing again. Neighbours have stepped in and other community organisations have stepped in to help people, too."

HIS DESIRE TO **MAKE A POSITIVE DIFFERENCE** ON BEHALF OF THE PEOPLE OF LIVERPOOL REMAINS AS STRONG AS EVER

KENNY CALLS IN

Reds legend Sir Kenny Dalglish has seen it all in football: from his own playing days as a world-class forward when club nutritionists were a thing of the future, to his dual spells as manager and his current role as a director and ambassador for all that is good about LFC.

Having an Anfield stand named after him in 2017 – the Centenary became the Sir Kenny Dalglish – certainly didn't change him and that same year he too made a donation at St Andrews Community Network for the North Liverpool Foodbank. Kenny joined staff volunteers from Liverpool FC who were on-hand to help prepare food parcels for local residents.

He'd already made it clear to the club that the stand with his name had to be inclusive, and to this end he came up with the idea of The Kenny Dalglish Community Suite, housed within – to be used by Red Neighbours with a focus on addressing food poverty, supporting the elderly, encouraging physical activity and creating memorable experiences for young people.

A spokesperson for club owners Fenway Sports Group remarked: "Having provided so much joy on the pitch, it speaks volumes for Kenny that even though his playing days are now behind him, his desire to make a positive difference on behalf of the people of Liverpool remains as strong as ever."

WHAT'S FOR 'BREKKIE'?

The pandemic ensured that tackling food-poverty became even more important. Liverpool FC quickly realised this and rolled out the Red Neighbours 'Breakfast Clubs to You' initiative.

The community programme usually welcomes hundreds of local residents to breakfast clubs at Anfield throughout school holidays. This time it delivered food parcels – each containing enough breakfast items to feed a family of five for up to three days – to school hubs for distribution to the most vulnerable.

Forbes Duff from Red Neighbours, explained: "We would usually be opening our doors at Anfield for local families, but we decided to bring the breakfast clubs to them instead.

"We wanted our local residents to know that we are here for them during the crisis and we will continue to support them however we can."

Normally Red Neighbours hosts breakfast clubs at Anfield for local families during school half-terms, as part of its commitment to food-poverty and education and creating memorable experiences for young people.

In October 2019, before the pandemic, Liverpool FC Women players Jade Bailey and Kirsty Linnett paid a surprise visit to give out free tickets for the upcoming FA Women's Super League derby with Everton at Anfield.

Other special guests that week included former Reds boss Roy Evans, ex-midfielder Ian Callaghan and Margaret Aspinall, chair of the Hillsborough Family Support Group.

The Easter holidays had seen Curtis Jones – now of course a first-teamer but then still an Academy prospect – meet with families to talk football and the importance of a nutritious breakfast. Joining him were team-mate Rafael

Camacho, LFC Women players Fran Kitching and Christie Murray and club mascot Mighty Red.

Curtis said: "It's great to have the opportunity to come along to initiatives like this – Red Neighbours are doing a brilliant job.

"Whether you're a sportsperson or not, breakfast is really important in setting you up for the day and it's great to see all the kids taking that message onboard and enjoying their food."

As well enjoying a healthy and tasty breakfast of either cereal and fruit and scrambled egg on toast, youngsters and their families had the chance in an LFC-themed raffle to win prizes like Under-23s match-tickets, Anfield stadium tours and an LFC baby seat donated by the club's official family partner, Joie Baby.

The previous year's breakfast clubs brought an appearance by goalscoring great Robbie Fowler, who lent a hand with serving the food, as well as then Reds defender Ragnar Klavan and goalkeeper Danny Ward.

Robbie said: "I'm a born-and-bred Liverpool lad and the people here have always been so good to me, so it's great to come along to things like this and spend time with the local community.

"We are lucky enough to travel the world with LFC and meet so many fans, but it's so important to give something back to those at home as well."

GLOBAL SCOUSE DAY

Every year on 28 February, people in Liverpool and around the world celebrate Global Scouse Day with not just food but things like music, art and cinema. The dish with the same name, though, is the headline act!

To mark the occasion last year Red Neighbours invited 12 youngsters from four primary schools in the Anfield area to the club's training ground to learn how to make the famous Liverpudlian stew.

The pupils – from Blackmoor Park Junior, Anfield Road Primary, Pinehurst Primary and New Park Primary – were taught how to prepare the ingredients and create the dish by club chef Tom Anglesey. And to top it all, Sadio Mane, Mo Salah and Joe Gomez also stopped by to chat before the kids were given a tour of the training facility.

Lucy Cushion, a teacher at Blackmoor Park Junior, said: "We had a brilliant time celebrating Global Scouse Day and it was great that the children were given the chance to cook the dish themselves. Our pupils are going to remember it forever."

DON'T GO 'HANGRY'!

The word 'hangry' is a mixture of 'hungry' and 'angry' and it's often used to describe how people feel when they've skipped breakfast. In fact there has been plenty of research to suggest that breakfast – particularly a healthy one – is the most important meal of the day, and that it can help young people to do well in school.

One study by Cardiff University found that kids who ate a breakfast such as cereal, bread, dairy or fruit, performed above average during national tests. The researchers said it didn't matter whether pupils ate breakfast at home or at school, as long as they had something.

It seems that, while each meal of the day is important in its own way, eating a healthy breakfast (high in fibre and nutrients) can help to reduce daily calorie-intake, guard against diabetes, improve brain function, and 'jumpstart' our metabolism.

The clue is in the word 'breakfast' – it's the meal that 'breaks' our overnight 'fast' when our body has used our energy stores for growth and repair while we sleep.

HAPPY BIRTHDAY RED NEIGHBOURS!

Red Neighbours marked its third birthday in 2020 and also celebrated many milestones, including the following food-related stats:

- More than 53,000 local people supported within the Anfield community.
- Over 13,000kg of food collected on matchdays over the previous three years, working with Fans Supporting Foodbanks.
- More than 1,800 local people attending the free breakfast clubs.
- Over 1,400 local pensioners invited to three-course Christmas lunches.

A LITTLE CHRISTMAS MAGIC

For Christmas 2020, because of the pandemic situation, Liverpool FC invited local families to enjoy its annual carol service virtually, from the safety of their own homes.

Meanwhile, as part of the club's *Operation Christmas Magic* campaign, Red Neighbours and LFC Foundation partnered with Cadbury to help promote its Secret Santa initiative – adding a chocolate treat to food parcels over the festive period.

First-team stars Alisson Becker and Roberto Firmino, plus LFC legends John Barnes and Sir Kenny Dalglish, all took part as 1,500 hampers containing Cadbury Secret Santa bars were sent to families in Liverpool and Knowsley.

In 2019, the carol service had been held as usual at Anfield, with club chaplain Bill Bygroves hosting as the choir from Notre Dame Catholic College stole the show with their rendition of *You'll Never Walk Alone*. Over 500 people were present, including former European Cup-winning defender Alan Kennedy.

Anfield also hosted Christmas dinners for pensioners, again thanks to Red Neighbours and its focus upon not just food-poverty but support for the elderly community and tackling loneliness and isolation.

Over 700 locals were invited over seven days to enjoy a three-course dinner and a sing-along with family and friends.

At the same time club staff worked together to create LFC's first-ever Christmas Giving Tree, made out of food donations, which featured on the club's official Christmas card distributed around the world. On display in the Main Stand, the tree was accompanied by a text-to-donate number.

SILKY SKILLS IN THE KITCHEN

Talking of Christmas, how about some festive fun brushing up on your culinary skills as well as your football flair, with a little help from Mona and her friends?

For Christmases past, LFC's head of nutrition has teamed up with Jürgen Klopp and his players to help children from local primary schools create the club's official greetings card.

Pupils from Florence Melly Primary School, St Francis de Sales Catholic Junior and All Saints Catholic Primary – all Red Neighbours-affiliated schools from the Anfield area – were invited to take part in the unique challenge alongside the first team.

Assisted by Mona, 12 youngsters joined the Reds manager and stars at Melwood, the former training ground, where they spent the afternoon building and decorating the gingerbread scenes depicted on the card.

Mona said: "It was lovely to welcome the children for the afternoon and we all had great fun helping with their gingerbread creations. The creativity and enthusiasm was fantastic and the finished articles are going to look great on the LFC Christmas card."

Once the children's creations were complete, they were photographed and printed on the front and inside of the official club Christmas card.

Nine-year-old Jenny Luo, from Florence Melly Primary, said: "I loved decorating the gingerbread. I wasn't expecting to meet any players, so when I saw them all it was just brilliant. I won't ever forget going to Liverpool FC for the afternoon."

The year before, Mona also made gingerbread houses with young pupils from St Francis de Sales Catholic Junior plus Gwladys Street Primary and Whitefield Primary School, before the youngsters went on a guided tour of the facilities and met Jürgen Klopp and the first-team squad as they headed out to training ahead of a Premier League game at Anfield.

SO WHAT IS GINGERBREAD?

Today 'gingerbread' means any kind of baked treat containing ginger and sometimes spices such as cinnamon, nutmeg and cardamom, and sweetened with things like molasses, corn syrup or honey. It was first cultivated in ancient China and is still used today as a remedy for stomach ailments. It's a traditional Christmas treat which can be stored in an airtight container for up to two weeks.

WE ARE LOYAL SUPPORTERS AND WE COOK FOR LIVERPOOOOL!

Who fancies a healthy eating masterclass at the LFC training ground? That was the awesome experience when a group of local schoolchildren were invited by Red Neighbours.

Mona led the interactive session which included making tasty smoothies and preparing and eating fruit and vegetables in a fun and inventive way – including making edible food animals!

In doing so the children also learned about the importance of a healthy, balanced diet and what their Liverpool FC heroes eat to maintain maximum health and fitness.

There have been similar LFC cookery masterclasses around the world, like one in Charlotte, North Carolina when the Reds were on their pre-season US tour a few years ago.

Again manager Jürgen Klopp took time out of his busy schedule to take part as the youngsters created a delicious and nutritious breakfast under Mona's guidance. The mouthwatering options included granola bars, fruit pots, sandwiches, smoothies and wholesome muffins.

NOS ENCANTA LA PAELLA!

Spanish ex-Reds stars, Luis Garcia and Jose Enrique, in a kitchen cooking a paella? It could only mean one thing: a team of Liverpool Legends were set to play a Barcelona XI at Anfield!

Unfortunately of course the big match – the fourth such LFC Legends game with 100 per cent of the proceeds going to LFC Foundation's life-changing programmes for young people – had to be postponed because of the pandemic.

Even so, Year 7 and 8 pupils from North Liverpool Academy, along with children from local charities Claire House and Wigzee Woo, had so much fun with Luis and Jose cooking Spain's national dish with help from a professional chef.

Paella is as tasty as it looks and can be very healthy with its combinations of golden rice, vegetables and chicken or seafood.

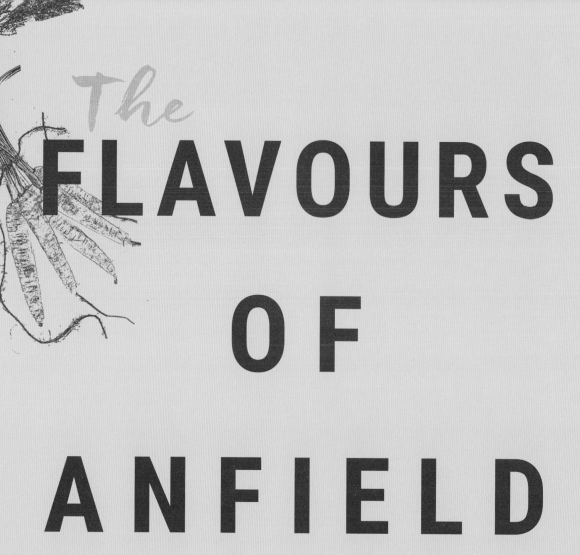

The
FLAVOURS
OF
ANFIELD

—

HOW WE RECOGNISE AND REACT TO THE TASTE AND TEXTURE OF
FOOD, AND HOW IT CAN BE TRANSFORMED BY HEAT AND DIFFERENT
COOKING TECHNIQUES TO CREATE MEMORABLE FLAVOURS

ROAD

Have you noticed that certain ingredients just seem to 'go together', without us really thinking about it, like chicken and tarragon, strawberries and chocolate, or even banana and chocolate?

These double-acts just seem to 'work'. They stimulate a physical and psychological reaction in our bodies and brains, often stirring memories of different times, places and occasions – perhaps even famous football matches – in our lives.

It's all to do with the combination of not just foods but their flavours, and there is a whole science behind it. In recent years there have been best-selling books written on the subject, like *The Flavour Thesaurus* and *The Art and Science of Foodpairing*.

That last word, 'foodpairing', describes a method for identifying these combinations based on 'neuro-gastronomy' – how the brain perceives flavour 'derived from the chemical components of food'.

We're not going into too much scientific detail in this chapter, but it's fascinating to take a look at the taste, texture and smell of food, the way the human tongue recognises different flavours and why this affects how we prepare and cook meals.

TASTE AND TEXTURE

Tasty, flavoursome, appetising, delicious, delish, more-ish, mouthwatering, yummy, nom nom nom... All terms to describe a positive food experience.

More specifically, our experience of a food's flavour and texture can be expressed by words which are either good or not-so-good, depending on the palate and appetite of the eater.

Food can taste (and smell) sweet, sour, bitter, bland, rich, hot, mild, sharp, salty or spicy, and sometimes more than one of these at the same time.

Similarly its texture can be crispy, brittle, ripe, stodgy, crunchy, creamy, tender, tough, moist, chewy, juicy, greasy or stale.

Interestingly, Japanese and Chinese cuisine prize the texture of food almost above everything else.

The way in which food is prepared and cooked affects its flavour and texture plus of course its appearance. There are 'moist' cooking methods like steaming, poaching and boiling, which use water in pans (or special steamers) and no added fat.

Frying on the other hand usually requires additional oil in a pan, while grilling, roasting and baking are ways of cooking in or under 'dry heat' in an oven.

CERTAIN INGREDIENTS JUST SEEM TO 'GO TOGETHER' WITHOUT US THINKING ABOUT IT

HOT PROPERTIES

The common denominator for all the ways that we cook is heat. This is what transforms food from raw to cooked, flabby to firm, pale to golden-brown.

When waves of heat – whether from a conventional oven or a microwave oven – penetrate the food, they cause its molecules to vibrate rapidly, which in turn creates more and more energy for the food to be cooked.

Heat-transfer occurs in three main ways: conduction, directly between two substances like the heat from a frying pan to a steak; convection, with the heat rising from below as with water boiling in a pan; and radiation, passing through empty space, for instance from traditional oven walls to enable the food on the tray inside to bake or roast. Incidentally, a 'fan' oven is simply one which also circulates the air through convection and results in a faster cooking time.

As always, practice makes perfect with every method of cooking – and thinking outside the box' can also prove to be very rewarding in terms of taste and health benefits.

When it comes to roasting, people tend to think mostly of meat, and certainly a dish like a buttermilk roast chicken for all the family takes some beating (buttermilk being a kind of fermented milk similar to natural yoghurt).

But how about roasting vegetables too, like broccoli or cauliflower or sprouts or squash or carrots, coated in sesame? Done correctly, this technique causes the veggies to caramelise (darken as their sugars are cooked over prolonged heat) for a simply sensational look, taste and flavour.

WHAT'S THAT IN YOUR MOUTH?

Without tongues we wouldn't be able talk, shout at the telly or sing at the match! Nor would we be able to tell what food tastes like.

This intriguing, indispensable organ of our bodies can be divided into five areas which are covered in little bumps which have cells called 'taste buds'. These detect five basic tastes – sweet, salty, sour, savoury/umami and bitter – and send that information to our brains.

Sweet, savoury and bitter tastes are triggered by similar chemical processes involving what are known as G protein-coupled receptors, while salty and sour are to do with alkali metal and hydrogen ions. Well, we did say there was a lot of science behind it!

As a rule, sweetness helps us to identify energy-rich foods. It's often described as the 'pleasure taste' because it signals the presence of sugar and thus energy. We'll look at different sources of sweetness later.

Saltiness (and we don't mean getting angry on social-media) is the amount of sodium chloride in food. Most people in the UK consume too much salt, but interestingly when we cut back on it, the taste buds on our tongue adjust

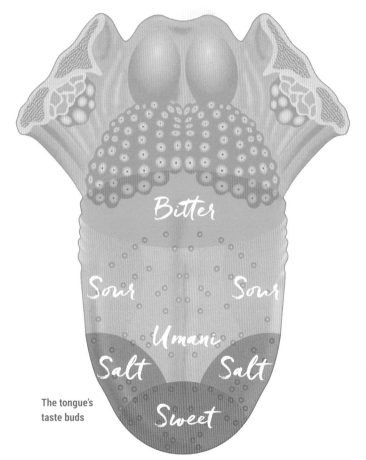

The tongue's taste buds

Anchovies are a common salty food

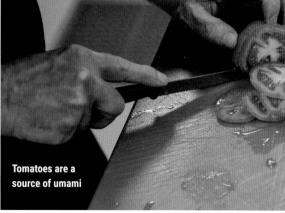

Tomatoes are a source of umami

so that we adapt to being satisfied with less. Indeed, using fresh herbs and spices in your food 'prep' cuts the need for salt. Common salty food include little fish like anchovies and sardines (when packed in salt), cured meats like bacon, *pancetta* and *prosciutto*, and condiments like ketchup and hot sauces.

Sourness is the taste that detects acidity. Too much – for example, sucking a whole lemon – makes us do that thing with our faces: mouths puckered up, eyes squeezed shut! Sources include vinegar, citrus fruits, wine, pickled and fermented vegetables, yoghurt and sourdough bread.

Savoury and umami are more or less the same thing, although these days the former word tends to be used to describe a class of foods or snacks. Umami is Japanese for 'good flavour' and refers to what we could call hearty food. Among the sources are tomatoes, mushrooms, cheese, seaweed and fish sauce.

The most sensitive of the five tastes is bitterness. This is a sensation which warns us that the food has toxic compounds. It can be unpleasant and so warns us about poisons. But it can also make some foods more interesting and, in the case of dark chocolate (in moderation) provide healthy antioxidants.

Citrus = sour!

Sugar cane

Sugar beets

THE SWEET SPOT

Cane or beet sugar is an obvious source of sweetness, but it can also be found in fruit, the sap or syrup of certain other plants, as well as honey and cocoa.

Sugar has quite a history in the port-city of Liverpool. A businessman called Henry Tate made a fortune from refining cane sugar which was imported from Caribbean plantations in the 19th century. He once lived in a big house on Anfield Road, a few decades before Liverpool Football Club was founded, and he gave his name to today's famous art galleries on the Albert Dock and in London.

Cane sugar, in its raw brown or refined white forms (when its fibres have been washed out), is grown from a tall plant in countries with tropical climates. Beet sugar looks like a pale sweet potato in the soil and can be cultivated in more temperate regions like Europe. Both varieties contain a lot of calories.

Honey is a natural alternative to sugar, produced all over the world by bees from the nectar of flowers. It has both nutritional and medicinal properties, but it's sweeter than sugar (and has more calories) so we don't need to use as much, whether on its own or as an ingredient for recipes. As a rule, the darker the colour, the stronger the flavour.

With its honey-like flavour, maple syrup is a wonderful topping for pancakes, waffles and desserts. It's made from the sap of North American trees of the same name.

Agave syrup comes from the sap of a type of cactus with big fleshy leaves native to Mexico. It can be added to hot drinks, breakfast cereals and baked flapjacks, but like honey it's sweeter than sugar so should be used sparingly.

As should stevia, also known as sweet leaf. This natural sweetener, derived from a South American plant belonging to the sunflower family and used in powdery form, is calorie-free but up to 300 times sweeter than sugar and has no great nutritional benefits.

Agave plant

MANUKA HONEY

MANUKA HONEY, PRODUCED IN NEW
ZEALAND, HAS MANY HEALTH BENEFITS.
STUDIES SHOW THAT MANUKA HONEY'S
BENEFITS EXTEND TO TREATING SKIN PROBLEMS
AND COMPLICATIONS FROM DIABETES.
MANUKA HONEY AND REGULAR HONEY HAVE ABOUT
THE SAME SUGAR CONTENT, YET OVERALL IT'S A
SPECIAL INGREDIENT ADDED TO SWEETEN TEA,
SPREAD ON TOAST AND DRIZZLE ON DESSERTS.

IT HELPS IMPROVE GUT FUNCTION, AIDS THROAT
INFECTIONS AND IT ALSO CONTAINS 22 ESSENTIAL
AMINO ACIDS FOR MUSCLE REPAIR.

The sugar refiner Henry Tate
once lived on Anfield Road

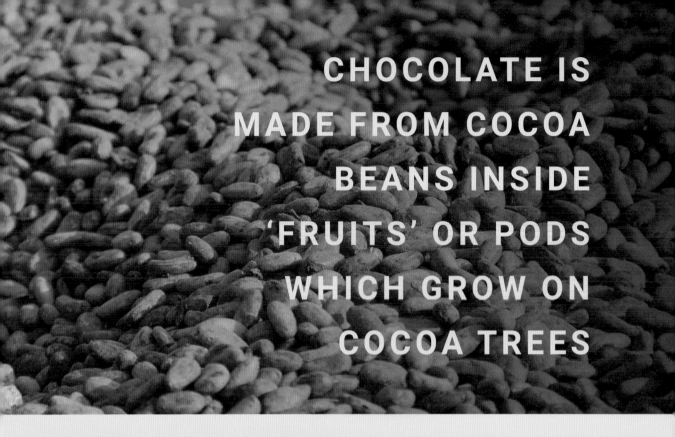

CHOCOLATE IS MADE FROM COCOA BEANS INSIDE 'FRUITS' OR PODS WHICH GROW ON COCOA TREES

Coconut sugar, now widely available in shops and supermarkets, is produced from the sap in the flower stem of the coconut palm tree, native to South East Asia. It looks a bit like brown sugar and has a strong caramel taste. Again, it should be used in moderation.

Which brings us to...chocolate. Pretty much everybody loves it, and the darker, more bitter-tasting variety does have some health benefits: less cocoa butter so less sugar and less calories; an abundance of micro-nutrients called polyphenols which are packed with gut-friendly antioxidants; plus magnesium and compounds called flavonoids which can lower blood pressure and protect against heart disease.

Milk chocolate is lighter and sweeter, with more sugar plus (obviously) milk.

Chocolate is made from cocoa beans inside 'fruits' or pods which grow on cocoa trees, originally in Central America. When they are raw, they are a greenish, light-brown colour but become darker when dried and roasted. Cocoa butter is also derived from these trees and used in the cosmetics industry for its skin-nourishing and hydrating properties.

In remains a fact, though, that too much chocolate is unhealthy because its high calorie content can lead to weight-gain if consumed regularly.

That's the trouble with sweet stuff: the more you think of it as being 'forbidden', the harder it can be to resist! Instead, try to take control of your intake and think of it as being an occasional reward. And remember: the more of the 'good stuff' you consume – particularly fruit and veg – the more 'acceptable' it is treat yourself with something sweet now and again. All those nutrients will help your gut microbes deal with it.

ON THE NOSE

Our tongues also work closely with our noses to identify flavours. In a recent BBC Sounds podcast entitled *A History of the Tongue*, the presenter was given a jelly bean by a professor in a 'taste lab' to put in his mouth while wearing a medical nose-clip. For a few seconds no air could get into his nose and he had to keep his mouth closed and chew.

When he took off the nose-clip, his immediate reaction was: "Oh wow – it's kind of flooded in!" The professor replied: "Notice there was just sweetness, [when you were chewing with the nose-clip on] and then...whoosh! In comes vanilla and other flavours – and all of that is coming from the nose.

"We move food around in our mouths with our tongues and that gives us a strong sensation that that's where we're getting all the flavour from – but it's not true."

He added that centuries ago one writer had described taste and smell as being the same sense, "where the mouth is the factory and the nose is the chimney."

ONE TEASPOON
OR TWO…OR NINE?

"Sugar is sugar," one dietician tells the NHS website. "Whether it's white, brown, unrefined sugar, molasses or honey, do not kid yourself – there's no such thing as a healthy sugar."

It comes in many guises on food labels, including dextrose, fructose, maltose, molasses and sucrose. If there are low-sugar or sugar-free options, try them instead.

Some items in the supermarket contain a surprising amount of added 'hidden sugar'. Take ketchup: one tablespoon may contain one teaspoon of sugar. Other culprits include some fizzy drinks, sweetened breakfast cereals, baked beans, pre-made smoothies and even some types of bread.

The table below shows typical examples of added sugar content in eight food products – not all brands, but some.

HIDING IN PLAIN SIGHT

Product	Sugar content in teaspoons
Iced blended coffee drink	11
Cola drink (can)	9
Fat-free yoghurt (carton)	5
Breakfast cereal (bowl)	4
Tomato soup (can)	4
Ragu pasta sauce (jar)	3
Oat granola bar	2
Ketchup (15ml serving)	1

Source: BBC News

SALTED CARAMEL – WHAT'S THE SCORE?

As successful double-acts go, salt and caramel is up there with Sturridge and Suarez, Gerrard and Torres, and Rush and Dalglish. Used to flavour ice-cream, yoghurt, chocolate, cakes, even drinks, it's addictive stuff – literally.

The sugary-sweetness of the caramel is enhanced by the flavour of the salt, and these 'fireworks on the tongue' cause our brains to release chemicals which makes us crave more. It's called 'hedonistic escalation' or the 'bliss point'.

The story goes that salted caramel was invented by a French confectioner in the late 1970s when he added creamy sea-salted butter from his native region of Brittany to a blend of crushed walnuts, hazelnuts and almonds. Now the caramel ingredients market is forecast to be worth around £3 billion by 2025.

Of course salted caramel should be enjoyed as an occasional treat. If you feel you've been eating too much, give it a miss for ten days and try to eat less sweet things. Chances are, the next helping won't taste quite as more-ish because your tongue will have new taste buds which aren't so used to the sweet taste.

In the canteen at the AXA Training Centre there is a 'trail mix' which combines roasting, caramelising and a tiny bit of salt for a similar incredible taste!

Check out our Sweet 'n' Spicy Nuts recipe later in the book!

SPICE THINGS UP

For centuries spices have been used to transform the taste of food all over the world. They were once as valuable as good and silver, and even today saffron is per ounce one of the most expensive commodities known to man.

Most spices, however, are very affordable and a great way to make even the most basic recipes taste new and interesting. All you need is just a pinch.

"Spices are rare things," writes author John O'Connell in his best-selling *Book of Spice*. "At once familiar and exotic, comforting us in favourite dishes while evoking far-flung countries."

Over on the right-hand page are some of the most popular in the UK.

Black pepper: originating from Kerala in southwestern India, it's actually dark red when fresh and high in antioxidants. A seasoning staple in countless dishes.

Cayenne pepper: a great way to add heat to any dish, this comes from skinny, red-coloured peppers dried and ground into powder. Probably named after a town in French Guiana in South America.

Cinnamon: native to Asia, obtained from the bark of several tree species and used as an aromatic flavouring in meals, breakfast cereals and beverages. Also used in traditional medicine as a digestive aid.

Coriander: its ground seeds come from the small fruits which appear after the flowering of the cilantro herb, while its bright, citrusy flavour is often paired with cumin in Asian and North African cuisine. Rich in immune-boosting antioxidants.

Cumin: an ancient spice consisting of seeds with a smoky, earthy taste, used in cuisine from Mexico to India to North Africa. Rich in iron, its health benefits include improved digestion and it may also help with diabetes.

Garlic: even if you use fresh garlic on a regular basis, having garlic powder around can be beneficial too – and it enjoys a longer storage life. It provides health benefits like helping to lower cholesterol and support blood pressure.

Ginger: spice with a zingy taste, popular in many Asian recipes but also used to aid digestion, reduce nausea, and support for our immune systems. Mona has often used to it make Christmas gingerbread with local schoolchildren.

Nutmeg: a fragrant flavour of Christmas, it comes from a dark-leaved tree which also produces a spice called mace. Lovely in spaghetti dishes and pumpkin soup, and for potato mash! It's thought to relieve pain and soothe indigestion.

Oregano: a staple of Italian cuisine, it was once native to the Mediterranean region but is now grown all over the temperate Northern Hemisphere. Also known as wild marjoram and technically a herb.

Paprika: made from dried and ground red peppers, paprika adds warmth and earthiness to a dish and comes in red, orange or yellow. It contains a compound called capsaicin with many health benefits.

THE LEGEND OF CURRY

For years, chips with curry sauce has been a favourite pre-match meal for many supporters in takeaways around Anfield, like lots of football stadiums – but how did it all kick off?

Curry is not a single spice but a combination of spices and herbs which is often fiery and robust, with a colour depending on the balance of ingredients. More turmeric, for example, will make it yellow. Curry sauce is produced when this mix is crushed into a paste and added to a liquid like sour cream or yoghurt, then served with vegetables, rice or noodles and sometimes meat.

Curry is often thought of as an Indian invention, but it's not well-recognised on the subcontinent. It probably started with the colonial British in India during the 18th and 19th centuries, who adapted local dishes to suit their own requirements, under the general heading of 'curry' (a Portuguese term).

The story goes that boatmen from what is now Bangladesh served on British ships during the Second World War and when some of them later settled here they renovated old cafes to sell curry and rice. Others took over fish-and-chip shops and served curry sauce to pour over chips – and so the British-Indian restaurant scene was born.

Chicken tikka masala was most likely invented in the UK in the 1970s and by the turn of the millennium it was voted the nation's favourite dish. Other curry faves on these shores – varying in degrees of strength and usually combined with chicken, beef or prawns – include kormas, bhunas, baltis, pasandas, dhansaks, rogan joshes, madras and jalfrezis.

Aromatic Thai curries are also popular and famous for their colours: red, yellow and green, in order of hottest to mildest.

The famous Asian chef Madhur Jaffrey first appeared on British TV in the early 1980s with a series tempting home cooks to introduce eastern flavours into their recipes. She's since revealed: "I started out not using the word 'curry' at all. It was too all-inclusive and our food is so varied in different parts of the country. Thirty years went by and finally I gave in. Curry is the way a lot of people think about Indian food, so if you can't beat them, you join them!"

HERB HEAVEN

Herbs, just like spices, can enhance the appearance, texture and taste of dishes. But whereas spices come from the dried part of plant, herbs are usually fresh, green and leafy.

We look at them in more detail in the chapter on growing your own produce, but they all have their distinctive flavours – hence their popularity as essential oils in aromatherapy – and they pair-up nicely as a garnish with certain foods. Examples include rosemary and lamb, mint and peas, sage and onion, basil and salads, dill and salmon, thyme and soups, and bay leaves and stews.

Herbs also have lots of medicinal value too. Did you know, for instance, that lavender oil can be used as an alternative treatment for minor burns and scalds?

SEASONING FROM SCOTLAND

While we love exotic spices from around the world, many impressive natural substitutes can be found in the UK.

The BBC Good Food Programme spoke to Scottish forager and 'wild food' consultant Mark Williams who revealed: "By opening our eyes and imaginations to the full extent of our wild larder, it's perfectly possible to make richly-spiced curries and pretty much any spice-led dish from around the world using fungi, seaweeds and the seeds, leaves, flowers and roots of common wild plants."

Mark made a spice blend from coriander grass, a herb called wood avens, hogweed seeds, dried spignel leaf, dried fermented garlic, wild carrot seed, a seaweed called dried pepper dulse and a mushroom called peppery bolete.

MONA'S TASTE TEST

"Normally when we talk about taste, we just talk about what we like or don't like. But it's so interesting to understand how important the tongue is as an instrument – and the nose, for that matter – and why we experience different sensations when we eat.

"How we prepare and cook food plays a part as well, and it pays to be thoughtful and curious. Think of how many ways you can cook potatoes – boiled, baked, roasted, mashed, fried – and how this affects their taste and texture.

"Heat, as we have seen in this chapter, transforms how food looks and tastes. It unlocks all those rich colours and flavours in meat and vegetables.

"There is a perfect example in our book's recipes chapter – the Rainbow Veggies. How you apply the heat to vegetables is crucial to how they cook. Something like a pumpkin has a lot of moisture in it, and if the heat is not high enough for long enough it will just steam and go a bit soggy. But if it's hotter, the pumpkin's natural fruit sugars caramelise, so it will roast and taste more flavoursome.

"Lots of fruit and vegetables have these natural sugars, so we should not add too much extra sweetness to our diet.

"Honey has the same calorie-intake as sugar but more value towards our wellbeing because it's antiseptic and anti-inflammatory, a kind of natural antibiotic. It can speed up the healing process in superficial wounds and burns by absorbing water and drying out the injury so that the growth of bacteria and fungi is inhibited.

"There is a big trend around manuka honey from New Zealand at the moment because of its high antiseptic values, but it's high in price too.

"We've actually had our own LFC bees at the club's allotment! Bees need to be somewhere safe, so they can live and not be irritated by any food smells for example, but they can thrive in an urban environment.

"There was a story recently about two beehives on a roof in the Liverpool ONE shopping centre, installed to nurture biodiversity. So far 160,000 bees have produced 80 jars of honey there – fantastic.

"Over at the AXA Training Centre in Kirkby we use honey and also chocolate – the dark variety – in some of our snack recipes. A good example is a 'power ball' made of oats and simply rolled in dark chocolate powder. Or you could roll one in toasted almonds or toasted coconut – there are lots of ways to be creative. Perfect for the snack-box at training the next day, and easy to store or even freeze.

"When people say chocolate is 'not healthy' it's really the process which is the issue: the lighter it becomes, the more sugar and milk is included. Also if you eat too much, your digestion suffers and you don't want that kind of uncomfortable feeling when you're out on the football field.

"Artificial sweeteners, some experts say we should avoid them if possible. The argument goes that they are not creating a benefit towards our wellbeing because they send the same information as natural sugar to our body – that sugar has arrived which needs to be digested to balance our blood-sugar levels – but when our body responds by sending substances to deal with it, there's nothing there because an artificial sweetener is just a chemical structure.

"Rather than added sugar – or salt for that matter – to season our food, why not think about herbs and spices instead?

"Many herbs have medicinal properties, every spice has a health benefit, and the spectrum of flavours is amazing.

"I find it wonderful that something like cinnamon, which adds such a lovely taste when sprinkled on rice-puddings or cereals or apple-pies or cupcakes, actually comes from the inner layer of bark on a tree. This is shaved off and when it dries, it naturally curls into 'quills' or cinnamon sticks.

"A bark with that flavour – which can also be used in air-fresheners, beauty facial treatments, and even to lower the risk of type 2 diabetes – it's just incredible what Nature provides.

"When you're really ill, of course you need professional medical care and sometimes antibiotics, but there are natural treatments for less serious conditions.

"Chilli peppers, which add hotness to so many dishes and also work well with dark chocolate, can also act as disinfectants. In the past when some countries did not a hygienic infrastructure, the chilli was a protection against stomach upsets.

"The substance which makes chillis hot is called capsaicin, found in the seeds rather than the red or green skins of the peppers. Today it's used in heat gels and plasters to reduce nerve pain in the body."

"AT THE AXA TRAINING CENTRE WE USE HONEY AND ALSO CHOCOLATE – THE DARK VARIETY – IN SOME OF OUR SNACK RECIPES. A GOOD EXAMPLE IS A 'POWER BALL' MADE OF OATS AND SIMPLY ROLLED IN DARK CHOCOLATE POWDER. OR YOU COULD ROLL ONE IN TOASTED ALMONDS OR TOASTED COCONUT – THERE ARE LOTS OF WAYS TO BE CREATIVE. PERFECT FOR THE SNACK-BOX AT TRAINING THE NEXT DAY, AND EASY TO STORE OR EVEN FREEZE"

BRING ON THE SOUR

THERE'S SOMETHING THAT THE KOP WANTS YOU TO KNOW…THE BEST BREAD IN THE WORLD IS SOURDOUGH! WITH WATER AND A LITTLE BIT OF FLOUR…MIXED WITH YEAST WILL GIVE IT STAYING POWER!

Good morning! (Okay, so just pretend if it's not.) The weekend's here (ditto), the sun is shining (okay, maybe that's stretching things a bit) and it's time to go out and kick a ball around.

Just before you do, though, did you know that while you're busy pulling off an Alisson-esque super-save or practising your 'no-look' finish like Bobby Firmino, you can also start to make the most delicious and healthy bread take shape? That's the beauty of sourdough, as we're about to find out.

It's become the most fashionable loaf 'on the market', on the shelves and in our homes. With its dense but springy texture and attractive dark crust, sourdough bread is celebrated for its great taste and nutritional properties – not least a convenient and steady sources of fuel from carbohydrates.

So, what is its story – and why does it taste so good?

DOUGH

ONCE UPON A TIME

It would be tempting to think that the upsurge in sourdough's popularity would mean it was a new-fangled 'foodie' fashion, but the exact opposite is true. In fact, in the beginning all bread was sourdough or at least a close relation.

Baking sourdough can be traced back to ancient Egypt and maybe even earlier and it is only in the last century or so that commercial baking and modern fermentation techniques have seen other types of bread become more common.

Historians believe that sourdough – like some of the greatest discoveries in history – came about as an accident.

In ancient times, farmers used to eat grains that had been crushed and mixed with water and made into a kind of porridge – perhaps not the tastiest or nice-looking of meals but easy to do, filling and good for your health. The theory goes that at some stage, the grain-and-water mix was left a touch too long and a farmer noticed that it was starting to bubble.

He or she had just discovered fermentation – and sourdough was born. This new bubbly mix was put over the fire and for the first time in humankind's history, bread was baked.

CHEMISTRY YOU CAN EAT

Making a sourdough loaf is the perfect blend of baking and science. Anybody can do it at home – it just takes a sprinkling of patience, a dash of knowledge and some good-quality ingredients.

During the COVID-19 pandemic, supermarkets and stores up and down the country ran out of flour quicker than almost any other product. The UK entered a sourdough boom as home bakers across the country decided it was time to put their ovens – and expertise – to good use.

How easy is it to make sourdough? The answer is 'very' and it is definitely worth the wait.

STARTER'S ORDERS

The key to a good sourdough is the 'starter' which is simply water and flour in a jar, which will later lift the bread dough. Gently stir and mix these two ingredients into a consistency similar to a batter, then let it rest for a while on a kitchen work-surface, for example, at room temperature.

The flour contains starch which is eaten by enzymes in the starter mix. When they do this, they release sugar in the form of glucose. Then along come microbes in both the mix itself and the environment, like wild yeast (single-celled little fungi) and other bacteria, to gobble up the sugar and give off carbon dioxide, lactic acid and alcohol.

The carbon dioxide or CO_2 appears in the form of bubbles, which will later help the bread to rise and 'brown' when it's in the oven, and keep its texture light and airy. The lactic acid (also found in dairy products like yoghurt and cheese) will give the bread its 'sour' taste, while the alcohol or ethanol will 'boil off' during baking.

After a few days of 'feeding' your new potion with more flour and water, it should start to smell a bit like sour milk or beer – a sign that your starter has 'activated' and the yeast is reacting nicely to the air, the warmth and the water. If it gets a watery film on the top, it just means it requires more flour.

Soon it can be covered and stored in the fridge, but keep your eye on those bubbles and keep 'feeding' it – you don't want the starter to fall asleep for good after all your hard work.

FROM FRIDGE TO OVEN

So you've prepped your starter and it's bubbling along nicely. Now it's time to harness its magic and add it to your dough, which is a mixture of flour (white-bread, wholemeal and rye can all be used), water and salt.

Place the dough on a floured surface and roll it back and forth with your hands, kneading the mix into a round shape to strengthen it. Slowly but surely it'll become easier to handle.

Add a little more salt, spreading it evenly throughout. Spices like anise, caraway, fennel or coriander seeds can be added, too, or perhaps mixtures of linseed, sesame seeds and sunflower seeds, for extra nutritional value. Then give the dough another good roll-through – this will help with the bread's internal structure.

Put the dough in a bowl and let it rest for a while with a piece of clingfilm or a clean, fresh tea-towel over the top to prevent it from drying out and to keep the warmth for 'proving' – the last rising of the dough before it's baked.

After an hour or so, place the dough onto a tray, re-cover it and, if you have time, leave it in the fridge overnight for the fermentation to continue. If you don't have that much time, leave it at room-temperature for a good hour before baking.

When you're ready, pre-heat the oven to 180°C and carefully place a bowl of water inside. Move the dough to a baking tray, put it in the oven, and let it bake for 30 minutes on the one side and another half-hour on the other.

When the loaf comes out of the oven, brush the top with a splash of water for a lovely shine. Let it cool for a good 30 minutes before enjoying your freshly-baked sourdough.

As you can see, creating one sourdough loaf takes 30 hours but only about 30 minutes of it is 'active' time. So rather than working your life around the bread, why not plan your sourdough adventure around your own schedule, like football at the weekend?

Spend the preceding week working on your starter, a few minutes here and there, then on Saturday morning finish the dough before you go off to football practice or a match. Then come back and put it in the fridge to prove overnight. Late Sunday morning, after you've been out and about, it's time to bake the bread in the oven. Roll on Sourdough Sunday!

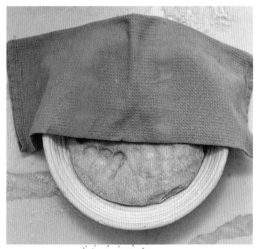

4 STEPS TO Sourdough Heaven

add starter
and salt
to dough

1.

CREATE YOUR STARTER

When you add water to flour, it will attract little smiley creatures (well, at least in our illustration) which are wild natural yeast (single-celled little fungi) and other bacteria in the environment – and boy are they hungry! You are now creating a 'live' mixture at the start of your sourdough journey.

3.

GET KNEADING

Pour some of the starter from its jar onto your dough mix and knead with both hands. Add some salt to make it more elastic. Roll through, let it rest, cover overnight in the fridge for a final 'proving' or rising period.

2.

LET THE WILDLIFE DO ITS THING

Starch in the starter mix gets eaten by our little red enzymes here, which then give off ('parp!') sugars. In turn, the sugars are eaten by our happy green yeast and bacteria, which then give off carbon dioxide, lactic acid and alcohol. The bubbles and sour smell are coming soon.

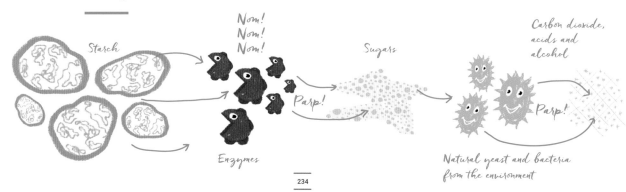

Nom!
Nom!
Nom!

Starch

Parp!

Sugars

Carbon dioxide, acids and alcohol

Parp!

Enzymes

Natural yeast and bacteria from the environment

4.

BAKE THE BREAD

This profile of a sliced sourdough loaf shows how it has risen in the oven, with the alcohol boiling off, carbon dioxide bubbles causing it to rise and 'brown', and the acids giving it a distinctive sour taste.

'Proven' dough ready to bake

Alcohol 'boils off'

Acids give sour taste

CO2 bubbles make bread rise, 'brown' and form crust

Holes! These are natural air-pockets

Crust

If you've spent a week getting your sourdough starter to bubble nicely, then more precious time perfecting your baking technique, the last thing you want is for it to go tough and stale. But if this happens, don't worry! The science involved in bread-making means that the moment it comes out of the oven, the starch in the loaf stops absorbing moisture and instead starts releasing it in microscopic amounts over time. To revive your sourdough, simply splash some water on the top and return it to a 100°C oven for around five minutes. This will allow the bread to reabsorb the water and make your dough lovely and soft once again.

SLOW AND SURE, NATURALLY

Bread has often had a 'bad press' in recent times for its calorie-count and the effect it can have on our blood-sugar levels. But sourdough is not just tasty – it can benefit our diet with its low GI rate.

Remember we talked about the 'GI' or glycaemic index in the first chapter, all those pieces of paper and logs thrown on the fire? It measures the speed at which food types affect the body's blood-sugar levels when eaten. Because the rise is small in sourdough, it means the sugar-levels are on a 'even keel', so carbohydrates are stored for longer and energy is released more steadily.

Sourdough is also a good source of protein and it's crammed with nutrients and fibre (often lost in some bread which is artificially refined) plus natural bacteria from the fermentation process which makes it easier to digest.

So basically the way that sourdough is made – slow and sure, nice and natural – can greatly benefit your sporting performance. You get a longer source of fuel, which is just what you need if you want to run and run and run in a relentless Jürgen Klopp team!

SOME RECIPES AND TIPS

For sourdough roast chicken, place four chicken legs onto a baking tray with lemons, olive oil, shallots, capers and onions and three slices of ripped-up sourdough. Roast at 180°C for 60 minutes. The bread will absorb all the flavours on the tray and give you the best croutons you've ever eaten!

In eastern Europe a good sourdough loaf is used as an edible bowl. Hollow out the loaf and fill with your favourite soup, stews or, as they do in Hungary with goulash or South African with 'Bunny Chow'.

Use sourdough as stuffing in a roast turkey. At Christmas, a baked sourdough loaf is fantastic when mixed with sage and garlic.

Sourdough is perfect as the basis for bread-and-butter or banana-bread pudding. When following a recipe, just switch normal bread for sourdough and its extra-special softness and absorbency will make a pudding to remember!

If you want to thicken a sauce, soup or stew then sourdough is much better for you than basic flour. Whizz up some sourdough in a food processor then add the finely-ground mix into your recipe to add instant depth and texture.

WHY SOURDOUGH IS SOOOO GOOD!

———

"Sourdough is very easy to make and costs almost nothing. People are sometimes a bit apprehensive at the thought of actually making bread, but in general in cooking you can't 'lose' or damage anything. Just give it a try and see what happens! The sourdough just needs love and treating well.

"At Anfield we've set up a station to bake our own breads, and for me it's wonderful to see that sourdough is 'back' because it's one of the oldest versions of making grains digestible for the human body, with the intake of gluten much lower.

"It's also a very natural product. We have yeast and bacteria in the environment – they're all flying around in the air! So you don't even need to be in a bakery. Just add a bit of water and flour together and your starter starts…living.

"It's quite fun when you explain to both children and adults what's happening with the microbes. It's chemistry you can see, touch and smell, too – like the sourness coming from the fermentation process. But you can always buy a sourdough starter kit if that's easier.

"So the sourdough is the starter which replaces baking powder or soda, or yeast. Then you add it to the flour, with any types of grains, and eventually you will have your 'proven' dough. When it comes out of the oven, you slice it and see all those little holes and bubbles, and that's what the sourdough makes.

"It's something you can enjoy on the morning of a match because it doesn't affect your digestion and make you feel bloated. It's quite a slow energy-release in terms of carbs, but it can depend on which type of flour you use.

"Wheat-based flour means a quicker release, while darker rye flours with more fibre structures will release energy slower.

"Sourdough is also really versatile. You can have it for every meal but in different variations. What I do with the leftover bread when it's getting dry, is make bread soup. Lot of onions, then chop the bread into small pieces and use vegetable stock. The flavour is beautiful and it's a nice recipe if you don't want to give too much dry bread to the ducks! Sourdough starters can also used for making focaccias, pizza dough, pancakes and lots more.

"There is nothing wrong with putting a little butter on your sourdough. It's gained a bad reputation over the years because our energy-outtake has changed so much. In the old days if you worked on a farm, for instance, you needed the calories because you were physically active every day and butter provided them and it was also fat-based. Nowadays you can buy everything and our energy outtake is not that high anymore, except when we do exercise.

"Also the fat-chains in butter are not the very best, which is why olive oil is declared as more healthy. But as always it's about getting the right balance between exercise and energy-intake, and also: when can I have a little treat?"

8 GREAT THINGS EGYPT HAS GIVEN THE WORLD

1. THE PYRAMIDS

The one still standing at Giza was one of the so-called Seven Wonders of the World. At 480ft (Anfield's Main Stand reaches 180ft), it was the tallest man-made structure in the world for 3,800 years.

3. MAKE-UP

Eye-liner has its origins in Egypt where it was made using kohl, a cosmetic derived from grinding charcoal-like minerals. The ancient Egyptians also used henna to paint their nails and dye their hair.

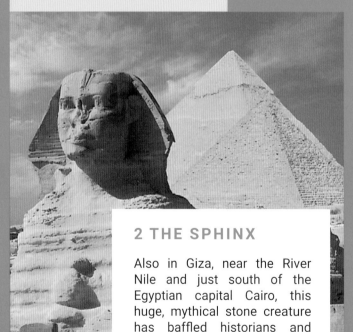

2 THE SPHINX

Also in Giza, near the River Nile and just south of the Egyptian capital Cairo, this huge, mythical stone creature has baffled historians and archaeologists for centuries.

4. CATS AS PETS

You often see cats depicted in Egyptian art like statuettes and jewellery. Not only were they domesticated, they were worshipped as gods and it was strictly forbidden to harm them.

5. WRITTEN LANGUAGE AND PAPER

When Egyptians became the first people to write their language down, it was in the form of hieroglyphics, which means 'sacred carvings' in Greek. And they did so on an early kind of paper called papyrus.

6. PHARAOHS

God-like rulers of ancient Egypt, from Rameses to Tutankhamun to Cleopatra. There were around 170 of them over 3,000 years of civilisation and many of their tombs contained fabulous wealth.

7. MO SALAH

Liverpool's own 'Egyptian King' specialises in breaking records, among them scoring 100 goals for LFC in 159 top-flight appearances – faster than anybody else.

8. AND SOURDOUGH!

Traces of yeast have been found in Egyptian clay pottery from 4,500 to 5,000 years old – and in 2019 an American scientist used them to bake fresh sourdough bread in a modern oven. His verdict? "The aroma of this yeast is unlike anything I've experienced. The crumb [pattern of holes inside the bread] is light and airy, especially for a 100 per cent ancient grain loaf. This is incredibly exciting and I'm so amazed that it worked."

Culture
CLUB

—

AS LONG AS HUMANS HAVE LIVED ON THE EARTH, THERE HAS BEEN FERMENTATION OR CULTURING. NOW IT'S MAKING A 21ST CENTURY COMEBACK AS WE APPRECIATE HOW IMPORTANT GUT HEALTH IS TO OUR WELLBEING

Earlier in the book we touched upon the benefits of a healthy immune-system and how it starts in your stomach with the right kind of bacteria. We've also looked at how sourdough bread is made by mixing flour, water and 'good' microbes in the environment like yeast. It's similar with creating yoghurt.

Now let's look a little closer at the magical process behind this. It's called fermentation and it comes from the Latin word *fervere* which means to glow. That might seem strange when we're talking about food which can be stored in the fridge, but it was most likely used to describe what happens when yeast converts fruit juice for wine, for example, or malted grain for beer.

For us, in simple terms, it means allowing health-giving bacteria to form in a sealed jar or other container of vegetables over a few months.

Because of its clear health benefits, food fermentation has become really popular in the last decade or so, and it's regularly used in the recipes recommended by Liverpool FC's nutrition team.

In top restaurants, fermented sauces are often part of some recipes and can take a couple of months to fully acquire their fantastic flavour.

TV chef Gino D'Acampo has revealed that his favourite pizza is a "traditional, slow-fermented Neapolitan recipe, baked on stones in wood-fired ovens." Fellow foodie Jamie Oliver calls it "a fantastic way to preserve food and also beneficial for our health – there's a whole world of fermented foods out there."

There's a lot of fermentation science out there too, known as zymology. Put

simply, it's the way a substance breaks down into a simpler substance and healthy bacteria is produced as a result.

Fermentation or culturing, as it's also known, promotes the growth and life-cycle of this bacteria to transform the flavour and shelf-life of ingredients. In doing so, it aids digestion by helping to strengthen your gut 'microbiome' which is home to 100 trillion or so bacteria and micro-organisms.

This is absolutely normal and natural. Microbes are invisible to the naked eye but found all around us, not just inside our bodies. While some play a role in causing disease, many do good things and protect you from illness. The challenge is getting the balance right.

Recently the BBC website talked to a genetic epidemiologist – a kind of disease detective – who explained that we are all "half-microbe, half-human" and need to take care not just of our cells but the bacteria, fungi, viruses and parasites which live in our nose, mouth and stomach. These, he explained, are "absolutely key to our immune system" and even to fighting viral infections such as COVID-19 – and fermented food can help with this.

On the map of fermented foods you can see that Asian countries are well-represented. So it comes as no surprise that Korea, Japan and China lead the world in gut-health or that many Western diets often need probiotics (products with the good bacteria) to counterbalance too much sugar or processed food.

"Diversity is the key," says one professor. "A bit of fruit and natural yoghurt for breakfast perhaps, or try a little *kefir*, *sauerkraut*, miso soup, or *kimchi*."

FOOD FERMENTATION IS REGULARLY USED IN THE RECIPES CREATED FOR LFC PLAYERS' NUTRITION

FERMENTED FOOD ACROSS THE WORLD

EASTERN EUROPE

Originating from the Caucasus mountains and literally meaning 'feel good', *kefir* is a yoghurt drink made from grains of the same name and soured milk. *Kisela repa* are turnip shreds fermented in a mixture of salt and water and eaten either as a side dish.

NORTH AMERICA

We think that sourdough originated in Egypt but today it's hugely popular in the United States and in Europe too.

CENTRAL AMERICA

Cortido is similar to kimchi and sauerkraut – a relish made with fermented cabbage, onions and carrots. *Pulque* is a Mexican beverage from the agave plant's sap.

GERMANY

Sauerkraut is similar to *kimchi*, with shredded green cabbage left to ferment in its own juices or brine for up to a month. Easy to add to many dishes.

NIGERIA

Small-seeded grasses known as millet are fermented for several days to produce a sour porridge called *ogi*.

ICELAND

Hakarl is a dish made with fermented shark meat which has been hung up and left to dry. Cubed and served with other food.

RUSSIA

Kombucha is a fizzy, fermented green or black tea believed to contain potent health-promoting properties. *Kvass* is a non-alcoholic beverage made from 'black' or rye bread.

FRANCE

Creme fraiche is a fermented sour cream used in sauces, as salad and soup toppings, and in desserts.

SOUTH KOREA

Kimchi is an ancient dish based around fermented cabbage or sometimes radish and flavoured with garlic, chilli and ginger.

JAPAN

Natto is created from fermented soybeans, like *tempeh* below, with a strong flavour and high fibre content. *Miso* is a common seasoning in soups and breakfasts, made by fermenting soybeans with salt and *koji*, a type of fungus.

VIETNAM

Nem chua is ground pork mixed with rice, herbs and spices, tightly-wrapped in banana leaves and allowed to ferment.

PHILIPPINES

Bagoong is a sauce is made by fermenting salted fish or shrimp. *Puto* is a steamed cake made with fermented rice and eaten with coconut and butter.

MIDDLE EAST

Surke is a hard cheese fermented from cow or sheep's milk and often used as a pitta-bread topping. *Ayrna* or *doogh* is a cold, fermented yoghurt drink and a national drink of Turkey with variations in Central Asia.

ETHIOPIA

Injera is the national dish – fermented bread made with an ancient grain and dunked into stews and eaten.

INDIA

Dosa is fermented rice and lentils made into pancakes. *Idli* and *dhokla* are breakfast dishes of fermented batter, made from rice, black beans or chickpeas, and served with chutney.

INDONESIA

Tempeh originates in Java and is made from fermented soybeans pressed into a compact cake.

Sauerkraut

IT STARTED WITH A 'K'

Many gut-health enthusiasts swear by the five 'K's which have been described as the "holy handful of fermentation." These are *kimchi*, (*sauer*) *kraut*, *kefir*, *kamut* (the name of a grain) sourdough, and *kombucha*. They all feature on the map.

While these food products may be 'on-trend' in the UK today, people have been harnessing the natural process of fermentation all over the world for millennia. Where and when did it all begin? No one is quite sure, but there is evidence from China dating back to 6,000 BC of a fermented alcoholic beverage made from fruit, honey and rice.

Perhaps fermentation among humans started spontaneously, back in the mists of time when a yeast microbe (and they've been around for at least 80 million years) landed in a bowl of food or pot of grape juice. Or maybe it was already present in some freshly-milled grain and just did its natural thing when the temperature and environment was right and no fridges were available.

However it kicked off, we've been developing and improving our knowledge of the process ever since – not just for pleasure but for practical reasons too.

Turning milk into yoghurt, cabbage into sauerkraut, or soybeans into miso were necessary in order for our ancestors to preserve food and make it last, especially during times when a fresh harvest wasn't available or cows couldn't be milked. They could use the flavours for cooking and make the food tasty.

Then in the 19th century a French chemist called Louis Pasteur explained the science behind it – demonstrating with experiments that fermented beverages result from the action of living yeast transforming glucose into ethanol (a kind of alcohol).

Kimchi

IN A PICKLE?

Pickling is similar to fermenting with one big difference. Both are methods for naturally preserving foods, but pickled products get their flavour from the use of heat and being soaked in an acidic liquid like vinegar, whereas with fermentation it's the result of the reaction between sugars and naturally-present bacteria and it tends to take a lot longer. And it produces that good bacteria.

LET'S GET FERMENTING

All vegetables are covered in the 'good' bacteria, lactobacillus. When you slice or grate them and add salt to their natural juice, it creates brine. In these conditions the lactobacillus multiplies and begins to break down the vegetable, digesting natural starches and sugars and transforming them into lactic acid.

In turn this creates the tangy flavour and sour environment which keeps the growth of 'bad' bacteria at bay, as well as acting as a natural preservative.

The BBC's *Good Food* website says: "As many people are cottoning on to the appeal of naturally-fermented food, it's becoming less scary and something we increasingly want to do for ourselves at home, rather than relying on industrially-produced versions."

Fermenting at home is simple to do and vegetables are a great place to start. Cabbage is easy, as are radishes, carrots, turnips and beetroot. The fermentation process creates a distinctive sour flavour, but why not experiment to discover what you like? Onions, asparagus, leeks and artichokes are examples of other fibre-rich veg that feed the good bacteria in the gut.

Other fermented foods include sour cream, yoghurt and of course breads such as sourdough.

FEELGOOD FACTOR

So we know that fermentation helps to produce good bacteria in our stomachs which contribute to a healthy digestive system as well as playing a role in the function of our immune system.

Too much bad bacteria, on the other hand, can result in symptoms such as bloating, constipation or diarrhoea – and modern diets combined with busy, stressful lives are often to blame for this.

Not only does consuming more probiotic-rich food bring the gut back into balance, it is particularly helpful if you've recently taken a course of antibiotics. And because our stomachs and our brains are so closely connected by the body's nervous system, it can work wonders for feelings of wellbeing.

For example, serotonin – a neurotransmitter which affects our moods – is made in the gut and 'binds' itself to receptors on nerve-endings in the intestinal wall.

It's not just for athletes – everyone benefits from the good bacteria in our food which helps to prevent stomach complaints, keep us energised and for footballers improves their performance in training and on the field of play.

There's more: health and beauty entrepreneur Liz Earle reveals that there is a skincare dimension to eating fermented foods – so you look better too!

Fermentation, says a spokesman from the world-famous Danish restaurant Noma, "has always been there – it kept people alive, it served civilisation... It's being responsible for life and watching it grow. It's a slow and patient process but it's also being rewarded.

"If people do it, they will become more invested in what they eat."

MONA'S FERMENTED FAVES

"Without fermentation, a lot of products wouldn't exist – we'd have no bread for example – and it's a very natural way to store things.

"In the old days when we didn't have fridges, we needed to ferment what Nature had given us so we could store things over the winter and keep them available. That's how it became established.

"It goes with the seasons. In our region, by and large, fruits naturally grow in spring and summer. So in the past, when they were gone, there were only winter vegetables and a period of no vitamins and micro-nutrients. But with the right preparation, fruits or vegetables like *sauerkraut* (cabbage) could be preserved for the winter.

"I'm pretty convinced that our ancestors didn't know about the health benefits. But out of this natural instinct to ferment food, to make things and store them, good things have happened for our bodies along with the positive impact on product-quality and flavour.

"It goes hand-in-hand with the feeling you get when you grow vegetables yourself – it creates respect for Nature and what it can give us.

"Eating fermented food can have a massive health-impact on the 'micro-flora' in our guts, and if that's in-balance we are much more unlikely to get obese than if we just eat junk food.

"I find it fascinating how fermentation works and it's such an easy process: the way a carbohydrate is broken down, yeast becomes involved and the bacteria start eating the sugars, and carbon dioxide comes out. The food actually starts living during this 'proving' or fermentation process.

"The process is the same but is faster or slower depending on the food. Sourdough grows quick, based on the fact that there is a lot of sugar in it from the carbohydrates in the flour. Sauerkraut has less carbs so takes longer.

"Going back to refrigeration, sometimes if I'm making sourdough I might be away from home with the team. So to stop the growing process I'll simply 'park' it in the fridge. Fermentation needs warmth to keep the process going. When we cool it down, it stops and we can pause it.

"To make milk into yoghurt – that's a fermentation process. We all know when milk goes sour it's not edible anymore. What happens with yoghurt is the same process but because of the right bacteria, it stays edible.

"These days you can buy kits with what are called 'cultivators' and little packets of bacteria culture to make fresh yoghurt – that's the quick version. In the past it would take a little longer but farmers would traditionally eat yoghurt or sour cream with things like potatoes or beetroot provided by the land.

"Fermenting drinks has always been really popular in regions of the world like Asia. Japan, a country with one of the highest life-expectancy rates in the world, specialises in fermented products like soy sauce and miso. *Kombucha*, from Russia, is a drink with a fermented base and it has such a massive wellbeing, health and gut benefit. You can taste the yeast, the smell of it.

"In Turkey they have a yoghurt drink called *ayran* which you can buy at kebab stalls. It's a sour milk in a little pot which works wonderfully with the meat from the kebab and maybe red cabbage and salad, and it's really good for your digestion.

"Over in Ethiopia you can find *injera*, a kind of fermented pancake with a sour taste. You just rip pieces off and dip it into stews and other dishes. I like it a lot!"

GROWING

your OWN

WHETHER YOU LIVE IN A TOWN, CITY OR THE
COUNTRYSIDE, THERE'S NO REASON WHY YOU CAN'T
CULTIVATE YOUR OWN HERBS, FRUIT AND VEG AND
ENJOY THEIR FLAVOURS AND NUTRITIONAL BENEFITS

HOME ADVANTAGE

Growing your own fruit and vegetables or herbs is a bit like managing a football team. You've got to have confidence in your own ability, make selections based on what works best on home soil, learn from the good times and the bad, and possess excellent communication skills – well, some people are convinced that plants *do* like to be spoken to!

Add a bit of patience too and the results can be most rewarding.

Cultivating at home or on an allotment – like experimenting with fermentation or buying frozen vegetables when fresh local produce is out-of-season or maybe too expensive – is both a practical and cost-effective way of having organic ingredients to hand.

Then there's the fun factor too: creating a window box of herbs or planting a few easy-to-care-for fruit and veg in a back-garden or on a roof terrace (please make sure it's safe and secure) and watching Nature do the rest.

Not so long ago, celebrity gardener and TV presenter Alan Titchmarsh wrote a whole book about it for the BBC. "For some people, growing their own food is a quality-of-life thing," he reflected, "an activity that the whole family can do together on summer evenings or at weekends...

"For foodies the big buzz is for 'fresh local produce' and it doesn't come any fresher or more local than from your own plot with the dirt still on – not fresh from a plastic bag full of gas or pre-prepared so that half the flavour has leaked out or dried up."

One of his counterparts in America, the hugely successful 'urban farmer' Annie Novak, says simply, "I want people touching soil, whether it's on the roof or not."

She continues: "I feel very deeply that people should garden. It's a good way to get outside. It's a good way to connect with whole parts of the world around us that we sort of block out most of the day when we duck indoors to work or sleep...

"If we spent more time outside, actively engaging in the richness of the natural world, I think it could make us all get along better!"

EXTRA THYME

"Herbs are the golden retrievers of the plant world — they run till they drop, and it's hard to dampen their *joie de vivre*," explained one writer in *The New York Times*. "In other words, they're kind to new or older gardeners."

It's quick and simple to grow herbs. All you need is a little space with some decent sunlight. Start small with a few pre-potted plants from the supermarket.

Having herbs ready and nearby while preparing food gives us an extra boost of flavour and increases the nutritional value of our dishes!

Basil: a source of vitamins A, C and K, manganese, iron, calcium, magnesium, and omega-3. Great in Mediterranean dishes, and also used as an essential oil.

Bay: grown in tubs and also 'wild' as a large shrub. Its leaves are a source of vitamins A and C, iron, potassium, calcium and magnesium. Perfect in stews.

Chives: its slender stems can be chopped and eaten for a fresh twist on salad dressings or sourdough. Rich in vitamins A and C plus potassium and iron.

Coriander: both a herb and a spice, with its leaves used for sprinkling and its ground seeds favoured in curries. Helps to lower blood-sugar levels.

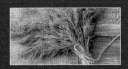

Dill: a tall plant with yellow 'cartwheel' flowers. Packed with flavonoids which have been shown to help reduce the risk of heart disease and stroke. Goes great with salmon.

Lavender: used in some recipes but better-known as a potpourri filler or moth repellent. Also a remedy for various ailments like insomnia, anxiety, depression and fatigue.

Lemon verbena: a favourite in fruit salads and drinks such as cordials. Good for weight-loss, restoring muscles, lowering inflammation, and strengthening immunity.

Marjoram and oregano: a herbal double-act thriving in sunny places and loved by butterflies and bees. A very famous combination with meatballs in Germany.

Mint: a classic, refreshing English herb which goes well in drinks, pestos and salads. Its leaves are anti-inflammatory and rich in phosphorus, calcium and many vitamins.

Parsley: great for growing in pots on the windowsill, it comes in flat-leaved and curly-leafed varieties, and it goes with all sorts of hot and cold dishes.

Rosemary: both a culinary herb and an ornamental shrub. An anti-inflammatory, its antioxidants boost the immune system. Another that works well in 'Med' dishes.

Sage: its leaves can be used like those of bay, and it likes being planted in a sunny, sheltered spot. Fab in the Italian dish *saltimbocca*.

Tarragon: quite large by herb standards, so one plant is all you'll need, and it comes in French and Russian varieties. Contains manganese, potassium and iron.

Thyme: another classic herb, loved by bees and chefs alike. Try cultivating it in a shallow pan or terracotta tub. It's rich in vitamins C and A and goes with meat, fish or starters.

THE PLOT THICKENS

Liverpool FC has a 1,200 sq metre allotment in the Tuebrook area of the city. It features reclaimed wood from the former Main Stand at Anfield which was used to create pathways and raised beds, plus mesh-fencing used as trellis for a wide range of vegetables and fruit being grown.

Local community groups and schools are regularly invited to help cultivate the allotment and it provides a place for them to learn about healthy eating, nutrition and hygiene.

A recent *Liverpool Echo* article about allotments revealed: "Some people take it up as a hobby and enjoy growing all sorts of wonderful fruit and vegetables. Some plot-holders have ponds with frogs, other keep honey bees and others grow giant pumpkins with which they enter competitions.

"Some enjoy meeting new people while others use them to cut back on their food bills."

From basic to big, your set-up will depend on what is available and practical to you.

If you do have access to an allotment, the Royal Horticultural Society advises: "Make sure you clear the ground, test the soil and plan what to grow when, to ensure a satisfying supply of food for the table.

"Getting to know your plot is as important as it is satisfying. Once you find out what the opportunities are – as well as the limitations – you can plan what crops will grow well, look good and taste great. With a bit of preparation work you can produce attractive and productive plots for crops all year round."

As well as space, you'll need some very basic gardening tools such as gloves, a trowel, hand-fork and shovel, plus a few plant pots or trays and some compost and liquid fertilisers, all of which can be picked up at relatively low cost. Then you're ready to go and get planting.

As well as the nutritional and financial benefits, there is also the fresh air, sunshine, birdsong, and colours and fragrances of your window box, balcony, garden or allotment – or wherever you can set up a little 'growing station' – to enjoy!

PICKING THE BEST FORMATION

'Companion planting' is the art and science of laying out a vegetable garden so that complementary types of vegetables are in the same bed. The aim is to create a harmonious garden by allowing nature to share its strengths.

For example, potatoes can benefit from being planted alongside peas, beans and corn. Carrots can prosper next to beans and tomatoes. The cabbage family (cabbage, broccoli, kale and Brussels sprouts) flourish when planted in the vicinity of beets, celery, dill, Swiss chard, lettuce, spinach and onions.

ONE EYE ON THE OPPOSITION

Much as we value and respect our wildlife – urban or rural – we still need to protect what we grow from certain birds and insects. To deter birds, the RHS recommends covering plants with netting or 'horticultural fleece' where possible. Aphids or greenfly can damage leaves and shoots, as can mildew. Again, check out sites like the RHS and Gardeners World for detailed ways to prevent this.

TEN VEG TO TRY

Beetroot: a tasty addition to any salad, beetroot are best to grow between March and July. They take around 100 days and are ready to pick when they're about the size of a tennis ball.

Blueberries: their autumn colours look great along garden borders in soil kept moist with rainwater. They're fussy about soil acidity, though, and are sometimes easier to grow in a container.

Broccoli: a fast and easy-to-grow crop, producing bluish-green heads for harvesting. Seeds are generally sown between March and June, the earlier ones in trays in a greenhouse or indoors, the later ones outdoors.

Carrots: grow-your-own favourites which come in all sorts of colours. They're quick and easy to grow, taking up little space. Sow small batches regularly for cropping from early summer through to autumn.

Lettuce: another affordable option, with seeds sewn in shade to keep the temperatures down. The leaves need around 50 days to harvest and it's best to grow them between May and August. Perfect to grow on the balcony in little pots.

Potatoes: grow your spuds with plenty of space between them – you can also use a container – between March and May. They take anywhere from 100 to 160 days to reach harvest.

Radish: perfect for eating fresh in a salad or as a snack, or roasting, radishes are best grown in plenty of space between March and August – they take between 22 and 70 days to reach their harvest.

Raspberries: a popular garden fruit grown in rows, containers or trained up a single post. Try both summer and autumn-fruiting varieties: just a few plants will reward you with plenty of fruit from midsummer to autumn.

Spinach: great for smoothies or juice, spinach thrives best in moist soil. It's another quick veg to grow, needing just 37 to 45 days to reach harvest. Grow between May and August.

Tomatoes: a packet of seeds costs as little as £1. Plant in the sunniest part of your garden and grow between March and July. They take between 50 to 90 days to reach harvest.

Mona's Message

"The LFC allotment is halfway between Anfield and the old training ground at Melwood. There they grow the whole 'palate' of vegetables – tomatoes, potatoes, carrots, cucumbers, sprouts, broccoli and so on – plus lots of berries. Recently they tried melons in 'poly-tents' which kept them warm and really worked.

"Gardens and allotments also give you the opportunity to use greenhouses, so you can start growing the seedlings earlier in the year, still getting sunlight but protected from heavy rain or overnight frosts. Poly-tunnels have the same effect but are more affordable and versatile.

"At Melwood we had herb pots wherever the balconies allowed. Now at the AXA Training Centre in Kirkby we have a rooftop terrace with the possibility of planting at either end for herbs, salad vegetables and berries.

"If space is an issue, you can get creative with things like pallets: bind or screw a couple together and put gutters between them, filled with soil, to grow climbing plants like beans, sugar peas and radishes.

"At home the wonderful thing about growing your own herbs or fruit and veg is that you don't necessarily need too much space – some containers on a windowsill or balcony or even outside your front door will absolutely do the job.

"There's such a feeling of satisfaction about planting things, caring about them, seeing them grow and then actually harvesting them, and also appreciating what they 'really' look like. So that tomato you grow might not be like a classic red Spanish tomato, for example, with no little dent or mark on it, but it's completely natural and might even taste better.

"Obviously as a population we are not able to grow everything by ourselves to fulfil the quantities we need, but it's not about that. It's a very nice way to give some respect back to Nature: to value products and see how long and also what it takes to grow them.

"Having herbs available, being able to give this green touch to what you eat, is so practical and convenient. They are there and you can use them, and it makes such a difference to the composition of what you cook or mix.

"Some rosemary, some thyme, some chives for a salad dressing, maybe. It makes your food so much brighter, colour-wise and also flavour-wise.

"How much does a small pot of herbs cost in the supermarket? Not much at all. It grows for months, years. It looks good, it smells good, it tastes good. So why would you not have it? Why would you use a dried herb mixture when in a very easy way you could have them there on your window sill?

"We talk in this book about all these different flavours, how things smell and taste. Herbs can be so aromatic. Try rubbing a needle from a rosemary plant between your fingers. It's such a strong, wonderful scent, so essential in a way.

"Rosemary is interesting because it grows well in this country even though it's normally a Mediterranean herb. It has strong, 'proper' branches which are amazing to see and to smell, and can survive different kinds of weather.

"It has a lot of health benefits as well. Along with an antiseptic value, research has shown it's also a 'cognitive stimulant' which can improve memory performance.

"Normally when we talk about flavour, of course we think about the mouth and how we recognise something by its taste. But it's so interesting how much impact our sense of smell has, too, and how many specific aromas there are.

"If you cover your eyes and smell rosemary, it's a wonderful 'wellbeing' smell which you'll remember. The same with lavender, thyme, sage, marjoram, bay leaves...all fantastic aromas. If you're growing herbs for the first time, try rosemary, thyme, parsley and basil – a splash of water now and again and that's it.

"Berries are super-easy to grow too. You can't really go wrong because they come back every year – you see them growing naturally in hedgerows, near fields or forests or parks. They don't need a lot of care, maybe just a little trim and clean-out now and again. It's just a case of getting more experience of growing them.

"When they're ripe, you need to pick them as soon as possible (be sure to soak them clean too) because they might not survive another night. We are quite spoiled because we can buy them any time in supermarkets, but in the natural world first come the strawberries, then the raspberries, then the blackberries, with the colours getting darker as the year progresses.

"Strawberries start out white in colour then get yellowy then slowly red, and it's the same with raspberries – they hang on the branch white then turn red. Blackberries look red in the beginning then turn black.

"Apple, pear and cherry trees grow new fruit every year – they just continue – but it's different with vegetables. A leek or radish is just for one particular year, if that makes sense – you pull the leek out of the ground and that's it. That's the difference between fruits and vegetables.

"I would definitely give it a go with tomatoes. If you don't fancy buying the seeds and planting them, you can always go to any garden centre and buy a little tomato plant and put it in a pot or plastic bucket indoors. Bags of soil are quite affordable.

"Then all you do is water it frequently – not from above because tomatoes don't like rain – and off you go. After a couple of weeks the plant will grow and grow. It might need a little stick as a support, and you might need to cut back the leaves now and again if it gets bushy, but that's it.

"As you progress you could have tomatoes in pots, hanging strawberries on a balcony, anything. To grow potatoes, buy the kind you prefer, put them in a container like a bucket or a 'growing bag', cover it with a blanket or towel, wait a few weeks until the potatoes go wrinkly and little roots are coming out – everyone has seen that with left-over spuds in the kitchen – and put them in the soil.

"Best of all, growing your own can be a nice family activity: each person looking after a different thing, then on a nice summer's day looking at what you've created together, all that greenery with some lovely red fruits hanging off – great for a snack or a salad. It's a lovely thing to do."

267

EASY RECIPES

EASY RECIPES

NINETEEN HEALTHY RECIPES BURSTING WITH COLOURS AND FLAVOURS, INSPIRED BY SOME OF THE MOST POPULAR MEALS AMONG LIVERPOOL FC PLAYERS IN THE KIRKBY CANTEEN

"We've tried to keep all of these recipes affordable and easy-to-do," says Mona, "using fresh, healthy, seasonal ingredients which are fairly simple to buy locally. They're very colourful and should taste great!

"Whether it's meals for the whole family or snacks for young footballers, it's showing how we can do things differently when we prepare and cook food, without having a messy kitchen or needing to go to four or five different shops or supermarkets to get all the ingredients together.

"Sometimes it pays to think beforehand about our meals, make some practical and logistical decisions, if you like, because time can be so precious. I always say it's better having a home meal with a lot of vegetables prepped the day before, than going to a fast-food restaurant on the day itself.

"The canteen at Kirkby is more like a marketplace where the players can choose their food-intake almost like a buffet system. But some of the recipes on these pages are the same if not very similar, only more geared towards family meals.

"There's the '9.30', so called because that's the time we normally serve it for the players in the evening when recovery times are very short between games.

"It's a kind of soy yoghurt with different types of granolas and berries on it – made with lots of love!

"It's very famous at LFC, so if Jordan Henderson asks for a '9.30', everyone knows what it is. But it can be for in the morning too, as a breakfast, or as a midday snack for school.

"One of my favourites is the 'Buttermilk Chicken'. It's just a whole chicken in a large zip-lock bag with a cup of buttermilk, a little bit of salt, and lime or lemon juice if you want.

"You leave it overnight in the fridge which makes the chicken moist and juicy, and the seasoning is wonderful. Then you roast it.

"You can also chop vegetables like carrots, potatoes, sprouts, broccoli, cauliflower, whatever. Drizzle some olive oil over them, sprinkle some salt and pepper. Put them on a baking tray in the oven underneath the chicken on a metal rack at 180°C for 90 minutes – the same as a football match!

"What will happen while it's roasting, the skin gets nice and crispy because of the buttermilk, and all the juices drip off the chicken onto the vegetables, so they're getting even more flavour. A complete family meal with a lot of vegetables, so easy to do and it doesn't make a big mess!

"Back among the players' favourites is 'LFC Tomato Sugo' [sauce] – another popular menu item at Kirkby.

"It's so versatile. You can prepare it in batches, freeze it and defrost it when time to cook is short, even use it for dips similar to a salsa. Just add some fresh, chopped tomatoes.

"It goes with chicken to make a lovely Mediterranean-style dish, and with a tiny bit of spice it can be amazing.

"It can actually be quite hard to find good tomato sauce, especially when the team is travelling to away matches, so we created a 'standard' recipe.

"There's nothing wrong with heating some tinned tomatoes – that's actually a good way to conserve tomatoes because they are ripe and juicy when they go in the tin, they last really long and they're affordable.

"It's more about the process: adding more flavours, cooking it for long enough. And we don't want a lot of garlic in the sauce, especially not on matchdays when it might make the boys burp – although that could make the opponents run away quicker!"

Veggie Burgers for Two

96 Kcal
/ 100g

WHAT YOU DO (FOR TWO)...

1. Pre-heat the oven to 180°C. Sprinkle the rock salt on a baking tray, place the sweet potatoes on it and bake in the oven until they are soft.

2. When the spuds are soft, cut them carefully open so the steam can escape, and let the sweet potatoes cool down.

3. Take a spoon and scrape the potato into a bowl. Add the bulgur/couscous/quinoa, then the beans, and mix it all together to form patties. Season the patty-dough with rosemary, salt and pepper to your liking. Chilli, curry powder or fresh herbs can also be used. Form nice patties with your hands.

4. Heat up a coated frying pan and let the patties sizzle till they have a lovely, crisp colour on both sides. In the meantime, prepare your tomatoes, cucumber, onions and toast your bun. At the AXA, a pretzel bun is the favourite.

5. Use any sauce of your preference to give the Veggie Burger the best finish. Put it all together and enjoy!

YOU WILL NEED...

3 spoonfuls of sea/rock salt
2 sweet potatoes, blanched (briefly boiled)
75g bulgur wheat, couscous or quinoa, cooked
80g butter beans or kidney beans
Pinch of salt and pepper
1 sprig of rosemary, finely chopped
Garnish (for the final build) of tomatoes, gem lettuce and pink onions
Bun of your preference

93 Kcal / 100g

44%
PROTEIN

Buttermilk Chicken

YOU WILL NEED...

1 whole raw chicken
250ml buttermilk
Salt and pepper
1 whole lemon (no pips)
Handful of parsley
1 XL-size zip-bag for marinating

WHAT YOU DO...

1. Place the chicken in the zip-bag bag together with the salt, pepper and parsley. Chop the lemon into rough pieces, squeeze them into the bag and add them afterwards.
2. Give the bag a good 'massage' and leave the chicken overnight in the freezer.
3. Heat up the oven to 180°C. Place the chicken on an oven rack with a baking tray (ideally with Rainbow Veggies) underneath and cook for about 90 minutes. The lovely, flavoursome juice from the chicken will drip into the tray and give your veggies an extra flavour boost.
4. *Mona tip:* the chicken is ready when you can pull off a wing super-easy – the bone simply slides out. But use a sheet of kitchen roll and don't burn your fingers!

WHAT YOU DO...

1. Wash all your lovely veggies, then peel the carrots, potatoes and onions, and chop everything to a similar size.
2. Put all the veggies onto a baking tray, adding olive oil and rock salt.
3. Pre-heat the oven to 180°C and roast the 'Rainbowies' for about 60 minutes.
4. *Mona tip:* this dish is such an incredible match with the Buttermilk Chicken.

Rainbow Veggies

YOU WILL NEED...

3 potatoes (new/salad)
1 red pepper
1 green pepper
1 yellow pepper
2 red onions
5 carrots
½ broccoli
200g sprouts
Olive oil
Sea/rock salt

33.9 Kcal / 100g

66.9%
CARBS

Chargrilled Family Salad

YOU WILL NEED...

1 Romanesco (broccoli-
cauliflower hybrid)
1 cauliflower
Handful of celery sticks
2 red beetroot
2 yellow beetroot if available
Handful of tenderstem broccoli
1 bunch of asparagus
½ radicchio
Handful of parsley
2 chillis
For dressing: olive oil, balsamic or
lemon juice, sea/rock salt

WHAT YOU DO...

1. 'Family Lover' – that's also what we call this recipe. The choice of vegetables here (below left) is just one way. Open your fridge and simply get inspired!

2. Wash the veggies, chop them roughly, add a little bit of olive oil and rock salt and roast at 180°C for 15-30 minutes until they have a lovely 'toast' on them. Don't worry if the veggies are still a bit crunchy – that's what we like in an amazing family salad.

3. Move the veggies into a big family salad bowl, add some rock salt, lemon juice or balsamic, plus a bit of olive oil, and give it a good mix.

4. If you have any leaf salads available, add them at the very last moment to make sure they stay crunchy.

25.6 Kcal / 100g

59.9%
CARBS

Kale
Chips

149 Kcal / 100g

KALE IS
RICH IN
VITAMINS
A & K

YOU WILL NEED...

Curly kale leaves
Olive oil
Sea/rock salt and pepper

WHAT YOU DO...

1. Wash the kale, tear into bite-size pieces, then let them dry on either a kitchen-roll or any clean paper-towel.
2. Pre-heat the oven to 180°C. Pour a little oil onto a baking tray, add the kale and give it a good mix it on the tray.
3. Roast for 15 minutes, then take it out, add rock salt and pepper and enjoy this amazing crispy snack.
4. *Mona tip:* this is a game-changer in a sandwich or on a spread!

Bean butter

154 Kcal / 100g

28.2%
CARBS

WHAT YOU DO...

1. Drain the butterbeans through a colander and feed them into a little hand-mixer.
2. Add parsley, lemon zest, the juice of half-a-lemon, rock salt, olive oil, and fresh black pepper.
3. Blitz it – and that's that!
4. This is an incredibly versatile dish. Move it to a Kilner jar (a glass preserving jar with an airtight lid) and store it in the fridge. It's a wonderful spread which can replace butter super-easy, and it goes wonderfully well with jacket potatoes, on a sandwich or as a little topping for crackers.
5. *Mona tip:* you simply need to try it!

YOU WILL NEED...

350g white butterbeans
100g parsley leaves
Zest of lemon
Juice of half-a-lemon
1 tsp sea/rock salt
50ml olive oil
Black pepper

69 Kcal / 100g

Star Dip

20.2% PROTEIN

WHAT YOU DO...

1. Mix all the ingredients in a bowl, add the lemon juice at the end and give it a little try – It might need a tiny bit more salt.
2. Season to your personal preference.
3. Rose petals are available in a lot of supermarkets or oriental cuisine stores. In case you can't get any, you could also use fresh ones. They deliver the 'sparkle' but will not minimise the taste and the culinary experience. Either way, you will enjoy this dip so much – we promise!

YOU WILL NEED...

250g of whole plain yoghurt
½ cucumber, grated
25g crushed walnuts
Handful of parsley, finely-chopped
Handful of chive, finely-chopped
Handful of fresh mint, finely-chopped
Salt and black pepper
Juice of half-a-lemon
Optional: rose petals

ZuCaCa

(ZUCCHINI AND CARROT CAKE)

230 Kcal / 100g

47.2%
CARBS

Whisk

YOU WILL NEED...

160g zucchini/courgette
160g raw carrots
4 eggs
50g brown sugar
75ml olive oil
Pinch of sea/rock salt
1 tsp baking powder
250g flour

Pour some more

Pour

Bake

Enjoy!

WHAT YOU DO...

1. Wash your veggies, peel your carrots and grate them. If the zucchini is a bit watery, place in a colander and drain.
2. Crack the four eggs in a mixing bowl, add the brown sugar and whisk them till the eggs are foamy. Add the olive oil, a pinch of rock salt and the flour with the baking powder. Mix all the ingredients to a nice dough.
4. Add the grated carrots and zucchini, then one last little mix and put it on a baking tray, covered with baking paper.
5. Optional: you can add any spices or herbs in to the ZuCaCa. We added a bit of cinnamon and it was delicious. But also curry powder or some parsley will work brilliantly!
6. Pre-heat the oven to 180°C and bake the cake for about 40 minutes. Stick a wooden skewer in the cake and when there is no more dough left, we are ready to go.
7. *Mona tip:* It's a mixture between bread and cake, suitable for all sorts of occasions – toasted for breakfast or even in the sandwich box. The consistency is lovely and juicy!

Shaker Salad

Your 'power salad' can consist of:
Dressings: honey-mustard, balsamic, yoghurt-lemon, sesame-soy, lemon-olive oil.
Leaves: spinach, rocket, mixed-leaf, cabbage, romaine, iceberg, kale, red chard, watercress, red cabbage.
Protein: diced chicken, chickpeas, quinoa, tuna chunks, halloumi, feta, mozzarella, eggs, prawns.
Condiments: croutons, nuts, seeds, chopped avocado, cress, bean sprouts.
Vegetables: celery, beetroot, carrot, diced peppers, cucumber, edamame beans, sweetcorn, fennel, cherry tomatoes, broccoli.

YOU WILL NEED...

It really just depends on what you fancy! With your chosen veggies, use halves and quarters. One of the most simple dressings is lemon juice, a tiny bit of rock salt, and a good oil – it could be a nut oil for a change – and fresh pepper.

WHAT YOU DO...

1. Just shake it! We've all had those times when we've tried to mix our salad and had more leaves on the table than anywhere else. The perfect solution is to shake it.
2. Take a decent-sized glass with a lid which can't fall off, like a Kilner jar or a big beetroot glass.
3. Add your preferred ingredients and just be creative! There a millions of options. You can even add quinoa, rice, pasta, couscous...
4. Perfect to prep for guests, for the office, to travel, or just for now.

36.9 Kcal / 100g

36.1%
CARBS

56 Kcal / 100g

91.2%
CARBS

YOU WILL NEED...

3 large red onions
60g white sugar
60g white wine vinegar
20g sea/rock salt
1 bay leaf
½ tsp fennel seeds
Pinch of black pepper

Sweet and Sour Onions

WHAT YOU DO...

1. Peel the onions, shave them on a 'mandolin' or just chop them finely. Then place them in a glass container with a lid.
2. Put all the other ingredients into a pot and heat it up, boiling for a couple of minutes.
3. Carefully pour the hot liquid into the glass container, put the lid on and let it slowly cool down.
4. Pickled onions! On sandwiches, with cheese or in your salad dressing. Absolutely adorable and so easy to make.
5. *Mona tip:* a must-have in every fridge!

Home Made Pasta

286 Kcal / 100g

58.1%
CARBS

YOU WILL NEED...

200g of flour
4 egg yolks
1 whole egg
Pinch of sea/rock salt
Large pot of water

WHAT YOU DO...

1. Add water to the egg yolk but only as much as it can absorb.

2. Sprinkle the flour on a clean work-surface and create a little 'volcano'. Gently add the eggs, then the salt, and mix with a fork.

3. Knead until the dough is smooth and soft and not sticking against the work-surface. Then wrap it in clingfilm, let it rest for 20 minutes and using either a rolling pin or pasta machine, cut the pasta to your preferred shape.

4. Make sure you have enough flour on your work-surface to stop the dough sticking!

5. Carefully bring a large pan of water to the boil, adding three tablespoons of salt. Add the pasta. It will only take two minutes so make sure you have your pasta sauce, pesto or just fresh herbs and olive oil ready to mix in!

6. *Mona tip:* this is a real favourite in our house – it's how my grandma did it!

LFC Tomato Sugo

30.5 Kcal / 100g

THE PLAYERS LOVE THIS SAUCE!

YOU WILL NEED...

1kg freshly-chopped tomatoes
2 tins of whole tomatoes
½ garlic
3 finely-chopped onions
4 tsp olive oil
Fresh rosemary
Fresh thyme
1 tbsp brown sugar
2 tsp sea/rock salt

WHAT YOU DO...

1. Heat the olive oil in a big pot, add the onions and garlic and let it sizzle.

2. Add all the tomatoes, brown sugar and the herbs. Add one tablespoon of salt and save the other for later to make sure the flavour is fine.

3. Let it cook on a low flame, otherwise it will burn too quickly. After it sizzles for around 90 minutes, you can see when it's ready when it has a shiny, silky surface and the deep red of the tomatoes turns a little orange.

4. *Mona tip:* cook tomato sauce in bulk and freeze it away in portions. It's great for tomato-based dishes like ratatouille or sauce for pasta and pizza, and loads more!

Crumble it

Just how good?

Peel etc

137 Kcal / 100g

11.9% PROTEIN

Pour in the mix

Add the crumble

YOU WILL NEED...

To blend:
80g ground almonds
50g almond flakes
50g cashew nuts
50g sunflower seeds
5g pumpkin seeds

For filling:
1 punnet of strawberries
1 punnet of raspberries
3 red apples
1 vanilla pod
1 tsp agave syrup

WHAT YOU DO...

1. Weigh all the ingredients into a bowl, peel and mix them.
2. We've used strawberries and raspberries in this example, plus apples. But you can use pears, rhubarb – the whole variety of fruits, depending on the season.
3. Put your fruit-mix filling on a baking tray, add the blended crumble and bake for 30 minutes at 180°C.

FOOTIE FAVE

Late snack

9:30

Muesli

Yoghurt

A nice bowl!

133 Kcal / 100g

45.3%
CARBS

Lovely oats

Granola

YOU WILL NEED...

2 soy yoghurts (e.g. blueberry and cherry)
2 tbsp oats
2 tbsp granola
2 tbsp flaked almonds
1 tbsp cashew nuts
2 or 3 raspberries
2 strawberries
Handful of blueberries

WHAT YOU DO...

1. Take a deep bowl, open the yoghurts, scrape them into the bowl and leave the spoon directly in there, as you can use it.

2. Take a new spoon and add all the ingredients exactly in the same order, and off we go.

3. Perfect to prepare and leave in the fridge. You can also turn it into a '4:30' as an afternoon snack.

4. *Mona tip:* this is our boys' favourite! The name was created because we serve it at 9:30pm as a little late-night snack to support recovery and help to refuel when time is short during the season, which it often is.

Sweet 'n' Spicy Nuts

YOU WILL NEED...

60g golden raisins
50g cranberries
30g pumpkin seeds
50g pistachio nuts
25g sunflower seeds
70g cashew nuts
40g maple syrup
1 tsp curry powder
Pinch of sea/rock salt

10.3%
PROTEIN

425 Kcal / 100g

WHAT YOU DO...

1. Pre-heat your oven to 180°C and prepare a baking tray with parchment paper.
2. Weigh all your ingredients into a bowl and mix them together without the salt.
3. Put them on the baking tray in the oven for 15 minutes and all the magic is done.
4. A tiny bit of salt, as soon as the tray comes out the oven, will give the whole flavour such a boost.
5. Store them in a Kilner jar or tupperware container.
6. *Mona tip:* perfect as a snack, on a salad, on yoghurt – just brilliant to have.

Golden Milk

(4 LARGE GLASSES)

YOU WILL NEED...

360ml coconut milk (any type of dairy-free milk)
360ml unsweetened almond milk
1½ tsp ground turmeric
¼ tsp ground ginger
1 cinnamon stick
1 tbsp coconut oil
Pinch of black pepper
Optional: sweetener of choice
– maple syrup, coconut sugar
or stevia, to taste

12.1%
CARBS

136 Kcal / 100g

WHAT YOU DO...

1. Take a small saucepan and add the coconut milk, almond milk, ground turmeric, ground ginger, cinnamon stick, coconut oil, black pepper, and sweetener of choice.
2. Whisk to combine and warm over a medium heat until it's hot but not boiling – about 4 minutes, whisking frequently.
3. Turn off the heat and taste to adjust flavour. Add more sweetener to taste or more turmeric or ginger for an intense spice flavour.
4. Serve immediately, dividing between two glasses and leaving the cinnamon stick behind. Best when fresh, although leftovers can be stored covered in the refrigerator for 2-3 days. Re-heat on the stove-top until hot.
5. *Mona tip:* an energetic, cleansing drink for all seasons!

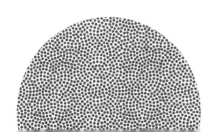

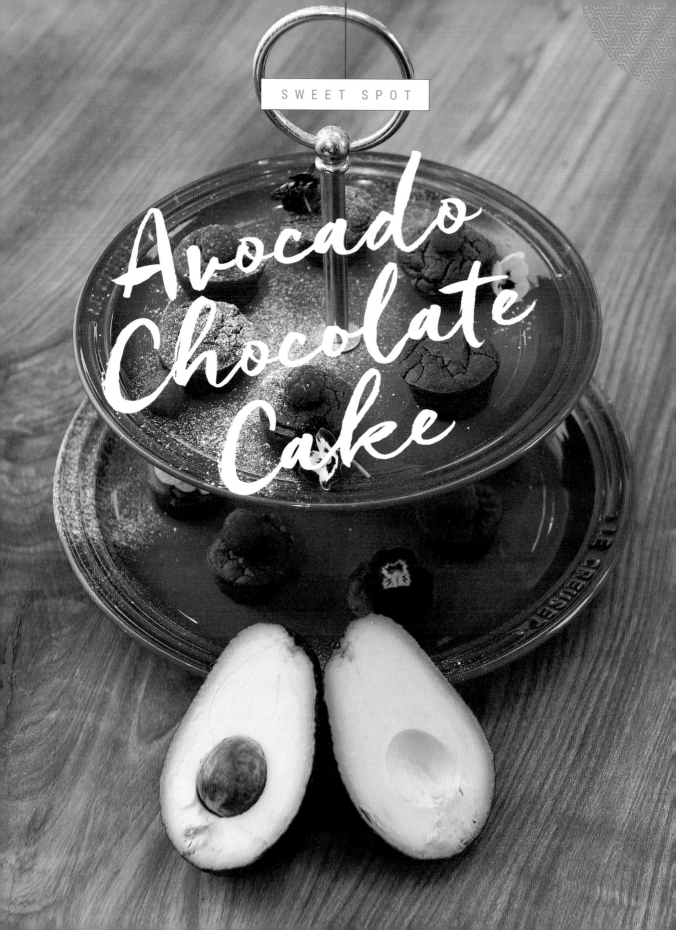

Avocado Chocolate Cake

Three cracking eggs!

Almond flour

258 Kcal / 100g

13.5%
PROTEIN

Avocado

Agave syrup

YOU WILL NEED...

3 whole eggs
200g almond flour
1 avocado (flesh only)
8 tsp cocoa powder
2 tsp baking powder
1 tsp vanilla extract
6 tsp agave syrup
160ml unsweetened almond milk

WHAT YOU DO...

1. This time we use a mixer or a blender. Add all the ingredients into the mixer, start at a slow pace and add the almond milk slowly. Mix until you have a lovely chocolate dough.

2. Pre-heat the oven to 180°C. Shape the dough into little muffin forms on silicon baking trays and bake for 35 minutes.

3. Apply the same wooden skewer test as with the Zucaca – it's easy to do and gives you a guarantee around your baking process.

4. *Mona tip:* instead of the avocado, try using a banana instead.

Knekkebread

25.5%
CARBS

370 Kcal / 100g

Mix your seeds

3mm thick

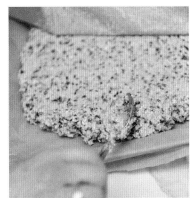

Roll then bake

YOU WILL NEED...

180g linseeds
140g sesame seeds
170g sunflower seeds
170g pumpkin seeds
100g rolled oats
420g wholemeal flour
150g wheat flour
25g salt
20g baking powder
300ml rapeseed oil
600ml water

WHAT YOU DO...

1. Mix all the ingredients well.
2. Roll the dough between two baking sheets into a thickness of around 3mm.
3. Bake for about 15 minutes at 200°C.
4. Take it out of the oven and the cut the bread to your preferred size.
5. *Mona tip:* This crispbread is unbelievably rich in nutrients and lasts really long. For breakfast, crumble over your salad, sweet or savoury with crudités or dips. We all love it!

PLANT-BASED FOOD AT ITS BEST!

43 Kcal / 100g

YOU WILL NEED...

1/4 butternut squash
1 zucchini/courgette
2 onions
3 carrots
1 clove of garlic
2 spring onions
2 tsp of agave syrup or honey
1 tin of chopped tomatoes
1 pack of tomato puree
3 tsp of olive oil
Sea/rock salt, fresh black pepper

WHAT YOU DO...

1. Wash and peel all the vegetables. Grate the squash, courgettes, onions, carrots and garlic to a consistency similar to minced meat (or just slowly chop the veg).
2. Heat the olive oil in a large pot. Roast the 'veggie-mince' then add the tomatoes and agave syrup and let it simmer till the veggies are nicely cooked and you have a 'saucy' consistency – it's always a good sign when the Lolo has a glossy shine.
3. Add rock salt and pepper, and spice for an extra kick.
4. *Mona tip:* this can be cooked in a batch and frozen. A perfect base not only for pasta but also a vegan base for chilli – just add the beans and you have a lovely minestrone. The options are endless and we absolutely love this recipe. Quickly made, great taste. Good for the planet, and the nutritional value is superb!

OUR GREATEST GOAL

A TASTE OF THE LIVERPOOL WAY

SUSTAINABILITY

HOW LIVERPOOL FOOTBALL CLUB IS SETTING AN EXAMPLE IN
SUSTAINABILITY WITH A NEW CHARTER FOR CLUB AND
COMMUNITY WHICH REFLECTS A INSPIRING GLOBAL VISION

In the aftermath of Liverpool FC's Premier League title triumph of 2019/20, journalist and Reds fans Hannah Jane Parkinson wrote with pride on *The Guardian* website about the club's "socially progressive values."

They included "supporting an end to 'period poverty' with free sanitary products available in every women's loo at Anfield" while "the *Reds Going Green* initiative has seen the installation of organic machines to break down food waste into water.

"The club even has its own allotment, which grows food to serve to fans in the Main Stand."

Mona Nemmer and her team recognise that a sustainable diet is closely-linked to lots of other things like community development, public health and urban planning, and their work chimes with this broader vision of changing attitudes and habits not just among players, staff and supporters at LFC but in the wider world.

It can be simple daily things like shopping locally, using water sensibly, reducing food waste and switching to multi-usable storage containers.

In the UK, the National Trust website sums it up like this: "By basing our diets on what's in season and locally-grown, we can reduce the food miles of our meals, help the local economy and even cut down on the need for plastic packaging. It often leads to a diet that's cheaper and healthier as well."

Experts at the famous Harvard University over in America paint a bigger picture, describing sustainability as a "multifaceted issue in which the food-production system and our diets play a crucial role. Achieving a healthy system and sustainable food future is an urgent matter that depends on global collaborative efforts."

As a sporting institution with a local heart and global pulse, Liverpool FC aims to lead the way in making a change and reducing its carbon footprint.

This includes becoming a signatory to a UN initiative called Sports for Climate Action, which aims to unify sports organisations to play their part in creating a more sustainable future by adhering to five key principles on climate action.

WITH ITS LOCAL HEART AND GLOBAL PULSE, LIVERPOOL FC AIMS TO LEAD THE WAY IN MAKING A CHANGE

DOING IT THE RED WAY

In January 2021 the club launched The Red Way – an easy way to understand how the club is contributing to a better future by pulling together all of its sustainability-related activity under one initiative.

An accompanying short film explained: "Sustainability – it's a word we hear mentioned a lot. Most people think it's just about the environment and while that's definitely a big part of it, it's actually about our society as a whole and how we can all act in ways that will protect the future."

The narrator continued: "The Red Way is how we're making a positive difference to sustainability by focusing on our people, our communities and our planet, and using our voice for good to help the next generation of Reds.

"All of our energy comes from renewable sources, which means we're not draining the planet when we put the lights on at Anfield. And we recycle all of our cardboard. In fact all of our catering packaging is 100 per cent biodegradable.

"We want to waste as little as possible. We even collect rainwater to look after our pitches and we turn food waste into green energy. Magic.

"We really care about what's happening in our communities too, and we know the difference great support can make. We help thousands of families across our city by making sure they have enough to eat. We also create fun initiatives that bring the people in our communities together so that they don't feel isolated.

"And our Foundation? Well they help children and families in so many different ways and not just on Merseyside but in different parts of the world too.

"Because sustainability isn't just about the big things – it's about making the little changes and adjustments to our daily lives that over time will have the greatest impact.

"Like caring about the people who work at LFC so that our staff live better in life and at work. We train mental-health first-aiders, encourage volunteering in our communities, and we even offer an electric-car scheme.

"A sustainable future is our greatest goal. This is the Liverpool Way of doing things. This is The Red Way."

OUR PEOPLE

432
VOLUNTEERING HOURS

spent helping local community projects throughout 19/20 season

26
EMPLOYEES
professionally trained Mental Health First Aiders

OUR COMMUNITIES

OVER
7000
SESSIONS

delivered last season by LFC Foundation to nearly

20,000
UNIQUE PARTICIPANTS

Red Neighbours facilitated the donation of

37.5
TONNES OF FOOD

to the North Liverpool Foodbank supporting

12,500
INDIVIDUALS OR FAMILIES*

* over the past 3 years

OUR PLANET

LFC is now
CARBON NEUTRAL
for our direct activities

653
NEW TREES

6000
PLANTS

1.5KM
HEDGING

at our new AXA Training Centre

We have offset

435
tCO2e

through Verified Carbon Standard reduction projects

Our allotment is the size of a
FOOTBALL PITCH.
It grows some of the food we eat at Anfield and is donated to local foodbanks

PEOPLE, COMMUNITIES AND PLANET

THE CLUB'S CONTRIRIITION TO A MORE SUSTAINABLE FUTURE IS BASED AROUND THREE DISTINCT PILLARS

Our People: reflecting how the club enables the people with whom it works to broaden their skills and knowledge, and make a positive difference.

Staff have been encouraged to volunteer to help local communities, totalling 432 hours in the 2019/20 season, while a further 26 individuals have been professionally trained to become mental-health first-aiders.

Our Communities: the extensive work undertaken by the club's Red Neighbours initiative and LFC Foundation, both locally and further afield.

In the 2019/20 season, LFC Foundation delivered more than 7,000 sessions to nearly 20,000 unique participants. Across the last three seasons Red Neighbours has facilitated the donation of 37.5 tonnes of food to the North Liverpool Foodbank, supporting 12,500 individuals or families across the city.

Our Planet: how the club is making a positive difference in the way it impacts the environment.

Vegetables are grown in a local allotment the size of a football pitch and are served at Anfield on matchdays, while the offsetting of 534 tonnes of CO_2 enables the club to become carbon-neutral for its direct activities.

Over at the AXA Training Centre, biodiversity has been encouraged by planting 635 new trees and 6,000 plants.

An online hub has been created for The Red Way enabling supporters to find out more about the work the club undertakes across each of these three pillars. It can be found at liverpoolfc.com/TheRedWay.

AXA TRAINING CENTRE

ECO-FRIENDLY KIRKBY AND ANFIELD

Anfield's pristine playing surface regularly undergoes 'clean-outs' during the summer months with the 'old' grass removed and new seeds sown ready and nurtured for the start of a new season.

The famous pitch consists of 97 per cent organic grass combined with three per cent of artificial fibres, with an irrigation system which speeds up drainage and allows for the entire surface to be watered in less than three minutes to stay slick and fast.

In turn these improvements helped the speed of the home side's game and coincided with a record-breaking run of home form.

Over in Kirkby the pitches at the world-class AXA Training Centre, officially opened during the 2020/21 season, are designed to replicate the one at Anfield. To support healthy growth, they contain volcanic ash and other organic products which reduce nutrient loss.

The design of the main building provides a clean, modern and warm environment with lots of natural daylight. Among the other eco-friendly, state-of-the-art facilities is a borehole which extracts groundwater to irrigate the pitches and tend to the landscaping on site. This ensures that the club's irrigation strategy is self-sufficient, avoiding the use of mains-sourced water for irrigation.

The Reds have also invested in a 'biological vehicle wash system'. This treats and filters out grease, grime, oil and grass-cuttings that can collect on vehicles and equipment and effectively recycles the dirty water to be used again.

TIPS FOR TAKING CARE

Create your own compost for your plants and vegetables using things like potato peelings, onion skins and grass cuttings – it is naturally enriching for your soil and will be gobbled up by an army of wild recyclers!

Don't throw away those glass jars – you can use them for storage or fermenting or even growing flowers or plants, and they look great.

When and where possible, buy un-packaged fruit and vegetables and more food items wrapped in paper or cardboard or inside cans or containers which can be recycled.

Take another look at those leftover veggies in the fridge – there are so, so many delicious recipes you can use them for!

Wherever you go, get into the habit of taking a re-usable bottle or container with you, for water, fruit juice or other healthy drinks. Remember: hydrate hydrate hydrate!

Stick with one re-usable, non-plastic bag for your food shopping – just don't forget to take it with you!

Make fewer trips to the supermarket and look out for more fresh, local, seasonal food produce. And consider eating less meat – maybe just a couple of days a week.

Why not try meat which is pasture-raised or grass-fed, locally-sourced and ethically-supplied, with a country of origin and a sustainability logo.

Check out your local charity shops for second-hand and vintage clothes and other useful items at a bargain price. And learn how to mend jeans that have become too ripped!

If you can, get into the habit of walking more often to football or to the shops, and think about cycling too.

Speak to grandparents or other people from older generations – you'd be surprised at how many amazing tips they might have for recycling and cutting down on waste.

HELPING THE PLANET ONE MATCH AT A TIME

GOING MEAT-FREE

In the summer of 2020 a global partnership was announced between Liverpool FC and Quorn, as part of the club's aim to foster greater food sustainability.

The sustainable meat-free meal-provider will collaborate with LFC to provide new opportunities for supporters to choose from vegetarian and vegan foods on matchdays, while also offering similar options to the players.

A spokesman said it would also help Quorn to "understand the positive impact our 'super-protein' can have on elite sports performers... Working with LFC and its world-renowned nutritional experts will be fundamental in the next phase of our sports-science research."

Captain Jordan Henderson and fellow first-teamers Alex Oxlade-Chamberlain and Xherdan Shaqiri helped to kickstart the partnership by discussing the environmental and physical benefits of switching to meat-free options.

They also mentioned centre-back Nat Phillips who revealed that he'd previously recovered from an ankle injury through switching to a vegan diet.

MONA: WE CAN ALL DO OUR BIT

"For me the key message in this chapter is to explain to families and young readers how as the LFC Family we have a duty towards supporting the planet and what we call a sustainable way of life – and that we can all do our bit.

"It's not about telling people what to do – it's just showing that sometimes little things can make a big difference for all of us. Like not wrapping things in plastic, if possible, making the most of re-usable containers for food, choosing more carefully and thoughtfully what we eat.

"It links back to everything we've talked about in the book: where food comes from, how it's grown, when to eat to it, what health-benefits it has towards our bodies, and why we should try to value and respect it a bit more.

"It's not easy but when you start growing things by yourself you realise what it takes – how much sunlight, water, care – and how fun and satisfying (and sometimes a little bit frustrating) it can be.

"Planning your meals to prevent food-waste and shopping sensibly – locally and in-season if you can – both contribute towards sustainability. And it plays a big part in our

cooking and catering at Anfield and the AXA Training Centre, where we also recycle as much as possible. Institutions like Liverpool FC have a big role to play.

"I think in every walk of life now you can see a lot of improvements: from the introduction of electric and hybrid cars to the phasing-out of plastic bags at supermarkets.

"As a country, as a continent, as a planet, we are far more aware of the environment and climate. Caring more – even if it's only little things like not throwing chewing-gum on the floor – can help make a change.

"Recent generations have become a little bit spoilt by the availability of different types of food from every part of the world all year round. It's not so long ago that seeing a pineapple in a supermarket was an absolute sensation!

"Nowadays when you go shopping, it doesn't matter if it's December or February or June, there will always be super-red strawberries, for example, there will always be green asparagus, perfect bananas, lovely berries and so on. Logistically it's incredible when you think about it.

"But if possible let's also try to think about the man-made environmental costs and damage. Take the air-miles and CO2 emissions to transport millions of avocados – which are indeed a 'superfood' but are also in huge demand – around the world, and the forest land and its wildlife which is destroyed to meet demand for production.

"Do we need to eat avocados to play football? I would definitely say no.

"Or take the 'water footprint' of meat – over 15,000 litres are required to produce one kilogram of beef. Compare that to the 322 litres of water needed for growing a kilogram of vegetables.

"It's said that 14.5 per cent of global greenhouse-gas emissions currently come from the livestock supply chain. I'm not saying we should cut out meat completely – not at all – but keeping our diets more balanced has to be a good thing.

"As I say, in the West we have been living in quite a generous situation – even with the terribly sad need for foodbanks – and sometimes it's easy to forget how blessed many of us are. But together we can make a huge change for the better."

WITH LOVE AND THANKS FROM MONA...

"We have made a dream work because of teamwork!

"A huge, heartfelt thank-you to Jürgen – a leader who gives opportunities, empowerment, and an environment to grow, innovate and improve. He supports and pushes you in equal measure. None of it is possible with him.

"Thank you to our owners for believing, investing and supporting what we do, and to our fantastic players – their commitment to becoming better each and every day is shown in their engagement, enthusiasm and passion to learn more.

"Many, many thanks to Paul Cuttill and his sensational team from Anfield – the best in the business, whose attitude is always 'Yes, we can!'

"To Tom from the LFC Academy – laying the foundations with our next generation of talent – and all the kitchen guys from AXA and Anfield: Andy, Tim, Tom, Rob, Mark, Dom, Stacey, Liam, Alec, Steve, Callum, Jamesy, Chris, Martin, Siobhan, our legendary Caroline and Carol. And everyone behind the scenes. They are the hidden superstars of our workplace.

"Thank you to David and all the team at Reach Sport. David, I have loved our conversations. To Marc, Mike and Tanja from MJK, Project B, the wheels in the background – without them, this project would have never started. To Matt and Kate from the LFC press team and their photographers John and Andy. They are always there – what a wonderful support!

"An extra-special thank-you to my amazing girls, Lorna and Aisy. These extraordinary women are the future in this industry and I couldn't be prouder of them.

"And all my love to the rock in my life, Peter, and my family! So much would not be possible without your support."

Mona